The Crazy Cantilever
and Other
Science Experiments

ILLUSTRATED
WITH PHOTOGRAPHS
AND DRAWINGS

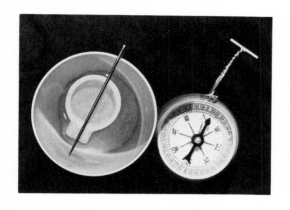

DR. ROBERT
R. KADESCH

The Crazy Cantilever
and Other
Science Experiments

HARPER & BROTHERS, PUBLISHERS, NEW YORK

Contents

About the Experiments   ix

1   The Crazy Cantilever   1

2   Pendulum Patterns   5

3   Mysterious Coffee Can   10

4   Centrifugal Force   13

5   Putting the "Fix" on a Wheel Race   18

6   Sweet Spot of the Bat   21

7   Tornado in a Smoke Ring   24

8   Whither the Whirl?   28

9   What Makes Sammy Swim?   32

10   Elastic Water   36

11   Errant Crystal Atoms   40

12   Light Popper   46

13   Bucket Bass   49

14   Dancers on a Gong   52

15   Pinhole Camera   55

16   Moiré Shadow Patterns   61

17   Pin Optics   65

18   Mirror Multiplication   70

19   There Was a Crooked House   74

20   Magnify It   78

21   Blow Bubble Colors   83

22   Compass Paradox   87

23   Electricity and Magnets on the Move   90

24   Wire a Telegraph Buzzer   96

25   Make a Motor   102

26 How To Stop Flickering Light 107

27 Electricity Drop by Drop 112

28 Rock 'n' Roll Spectrum 117

29 Nuclear Vapor Trails 121

30 Dominoes and Atomic Fission 125

31 Nuclear Drop in a Bottle 131

32 A Hole in the Hand 136

33 Seeing Is Disbelieving 138

34 Beautiful Colors within Your Eyes 142

35 Find Your Latitude 147

36 Find Your Longitude 152

37 Make a Chunk of Blue Sky 157

38 Measure the Thickness
   of the Atmosphere 161

39 Morning-Glory Gravity 167

40 Ballooning Universe 172

About the Experiments

This book contains forty science experiments and demonstrations you can perform at home. Inexpensive and easy-to-get materials are used throughout. Undoubtedly you already have much of the needed equipment. All of the experiments are safe —science needs no acids or explosives to make it interesting.

These experiments are intended to provide practice in careful observation, sound experimentation, and clear thinking. Science is much more than "Gee whiz!" It digs into the basic reasons behind all physical phenomena—the amazing, the curious, and the commonplace.

You can perform the experiments in any order

you choose, as each is a self-contained unit. Some are short and easy, others are longer and require greater skill. Each experiment or demonstration should suggest still other things for you to do.

The experiments need not be done in the manner suggested. You may be able to arrange better apparatus or develop improved experimental techniques.

We all can profit from greater knowledge of science and its methods, whether we intend to be scientists or not. In the world of today, intelligent citizenship requires scientific understanding by all.

The Crazy Cantilever
and Other
Science Experiments

1   The Crazy Cantilever

Take a stack of five or six books that are all the same size. Place them in a straight pile at the edge of a table. How far out over the edge of the table do you think you can place the top book?

The idea is to build a Leaning Tower of Books and to make the top of the tower lean out over the table's edge as far as possible.

This is a problem of balance, a problem that involves the center of gravity of each book and of the pile as a whole. Any object behaves as if all its weight were located at a special point. This point is called the center of gravity. For any symmetrical object such as a book, the center of gravity is located at its center. A single book will balance as long as its center of gravity remains over the table.

The center of gravity of the entire Leaning Tower of Books is more complicated to locate. But you might guess that as long as this new center of gravity does not extend beyond the edge of the table, the tower will stand. Otherwise, it will fall.

When the books are piled in a straight stack, the center of gravity of the books is at the center of the stack. The entire pile may be moved out over the table's edge until half the length of the stack of books protrudes beyond the edge, but no farther. The top book overhangs the table's edge by only half its length.

There is a better approach. Start with the top book in the stack and work down. The top book may protrude almost half its length beyond the edge of the second book from the top. Now, holding all the lower books in place, push the top two out as far as possible beyond the edge of the third book from the top. Then push the top three books out as far as possible over the edge of the fourth from the top, and so on, until you reach the bottom book in the pile. As a last step, move the whole pile out as far as you can over the table's edge.

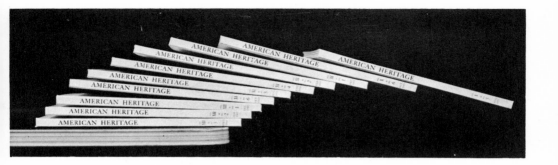

This time the top book extends so far out that its inner edge is completely beyond the edge of the table. You will find that this can be done easily with a pile of five or more books. It can also be done with four, but this is quite a trick.

The stack of books makes a crazy cantilever. The books look as if they should topple, but they don't.

Notice that the amount of overhang from one book to the next becomes smaller and smaller as you approach the bottom of the pile. With a sufficient number of books, you can see the graceful arching line of the outside edges that curves in toward the table.

Now let's analyze the problem mathematically, starting again with the top book in the pile. We found the top book could extend nearly half a length beyond the second and still balance. In this position the center of gravity of the top book is

3

directly above the outside edge of the second book. The center of gravity of the top two books, taken together, lies midway between their centers. The two books will not topple so long as their center of gravity does not protrude beyond the edge of the third book. This means that there may be a one-quarter length overhang of the second book beyond the edge of the third.

Now, the top *three* books must be thought of as a unit. Since the top two books have twice the weight of the third book, the center of gravity of the combination of three will be twice as close to the center of gravity of the top two than it is to the center of gravity of the third. This fixes the center of gravity of the three books one-sixth of a length in from the outside edge of the third book. This is the maximum overhang of the third book beyond the edge of the fourth.

Proceeding in this way, the extension of each book in the pile beyond the edge of the next one below turns out to be 1/2, 1/4, 1/6, 1/8, 1/10, 1/12, 1/14, 1/16, 1/18 lengths, and so on, for as many books as you have. For a total of four books, the maximum overhang is $1/2 + 1/4 + 1/6 + 1/8 = 25/24$ book lengths. For five books, the overhang is 137/120, or 1.14 book lengths.

4

Use as many books of the same size as you please, ten, fifteen, or even a hundred, and the top book can always be placed farther and farther beyond the table's edge. Although the overhang of each additional book at the bottom of the pile must be smaller and smaller, a sufficient number of books can extend the cantilever far beyond the edge of the table. Unfortunately, there probably aren't enough books in existence to give an overhang of five or six book lengths.

2   Pendulum Patterns

Scientific experiments sometimes give results that are fascinating and beautiful as well as instructive. Such is the case with the famous Lissajous figures.

Jules A. Lissajous, a nineteenth-century French scientist, first made the pretty patterns which bear his name. He used tuning forks and mirrors in his experiment. Let's do the same experiment, but use a pendulum and a sheet of black paper.

The pendulum bob will be a paper cup full of salt. Suspend the cup several feet from the floor by means of a Y-shaped arrangement of string tied to two chairs. Make the top two branches of the Y out of one length of string, the bottom part of the Y with another piece.

Make a hole in the bottom of the cup with a small nail. This will allow the salt to run out onto the black paper and trace the motion of the pendulum bob.

Pull the cup of salt a bit to one side and let go. An intricate Lissajous pattern in salt will be formed. A different shape can be made by starting the pendulum in a different direction.

An almost endless variety of fascinating geometrical figures can be made by shifting the junction in the Y either up or down. Try especially making the bottom leg of the Y quite short compared to the upper branches of the Y.

The Y-shaped pendulum cord really makes two pendulums in one. One pendulum operates when the cup is released along a line perpendicular to the two points of support. The length of this pendulum is the distance from the cup to the overhead support. The other pendulum is at work when the cup is released on a line with the two points of

6

support. This pendulum is shorter. It is only as long as the distance between the cup and the junction in the Y, since in this case the upper parts of the Y do not move.

A pendulum bob hung on a long string takes longer to swing back and forth than one hung on a shorter string. Because of this, the Y-shaped string provides a fast-moving pendulum in one direction and a slower-moving pendulum in the other.

When the salt bucket is started at an angle, both the fast and slow pendulums operate simultaneously. The curving pattern of salt results from the interplay of these two motions. Scientifically

speaking, the compound pendulum adds two vibrations which are at right angles to one another.

Relatively simple Lissajous patterns are produced when the ratio of the periods of the two pendulums (the time taken for a single swing back and forth) is a simple one such as 1 to 2, 2 to 3, 1 to 3, 3 to 4, or 4 to 5. It is this ratio that is changed when the junction in the Y is moved up or down.

When you achieve pendulum periods which are a ratio of whole numbers, the salt pattern will repeat itself over and over again. Otherwise, the figure will not be repeated, and the pattern will become more and more complicated as the salt

continues to flow. Eventually you will have nothing but a smear of salt.

3   Mysterious Coffee Can

Do you like to play tricks on your friends? If so, try this one. Roll a coffee can across the floor and, at your command, it will mysteriously stop and roll back to you.

Of course there is a logical explanation for this, but someone watching may be completely baffled.

First, find a coffee can. A round oatmeal box will do just as well. Punch two holes close together at the center of the bottom and top of the can. Cut a strong rubber band in two. Lead it through the holes and across the inside of the can. Tie the band together on the outside so that it is taut.

Now find one or two small weights. Bolts or nuts will be fine. Attach these to a short length of wire and hook this to the center of one strand of the rubber band inside the can.

10

Close the lid again and your mystery can is ready to perform. Roll it across a floor with a smooth, hard surface. After coming to a stop, it will then roll back to you, for no apparent reason. If it is a little reluctant to behave, "wind" it up in advance by turning it in your hands in the same direction it will roll on its outward trip.

11

This toy beautifully illustrates the fundamental physical idea of energy. When you push the can away from you, it is given energy of motion. As the can rolls, the rubber band near the top and bottom of the can turns around and around. The weight at the center, however, keeps the middle of the rubber band from turning. The result is that the band twists tighter and tighter.

Energy is required to twist the rubber band. This energy comes from the rolling energy of the can. When the twisted band has taken up as much of the rolling energy as possible, the can must stop.

Now you have a coffee can with a twisted rubber band inside it. This has more energy than a similar can without a twisted rubber band. The energy of the twisted band now starts the coffee can rolling back to you. The energy stolen by the band is transformed into energy of motion and returned to the can.

Sometimes atoms are like coffee cans with twisted rubber bands inside. They have more energy than normal. The coffee can gets rid of this extra energy by rolling back to you. The atoms expend their extra energy by creating and emitting particles of light or matter.

4 Centrifugal Force

A potato, a spool, a spoon, and a length of twine can be used to demonstrate what happens when

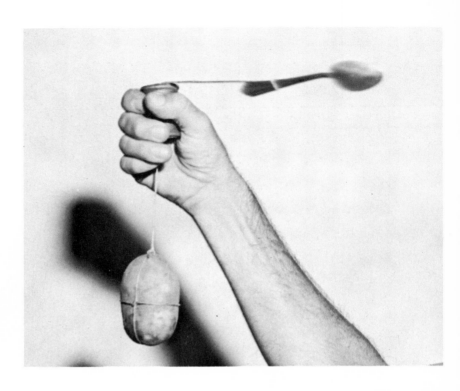

an object—any object—moves in a circular path.

Tie one end of a four-foot length of strong twine to a medium-sized potato. Thread the other end of the twine through the hole in the spool and tie it securely to the spoon. Hold the spool so that the potato hangs freely beneath it and the spoon so that it is a short distance from the spool. Now give the spool a quick circular motion so that the spoon will swing around in a small horizontal circle.

14

If you swing the spoon rapidly, the potato will rise all the way up to the bottom of the spool. If the spoon is now swung more slowly, the potato will move downward. You will find that at one particular speed the potato will neither move up nor down. The spoon is now in a circular orbit.

This completes the experiment, but from these simple observations much can be learned.

"Centrifugal" means "away from the center," literally, "fleeing (that's the "fugal" part of the word) the center" (centri). There is another important word to learn. It is the word "centripetal," which means "moving toward the center."

When we observe the action of the potato and the spoon, let us be sure not to confuse centrifugal with centripetal forces.

Think about the spoon when it is moving along a circular path and the potato moves neither up nor down. Gravity pulls down on the potato, that is certain. The potato pulls on the twine, and the twine, in turn, exerts an inward force on the spoon. This inward force is a *centripetal* force *on the spoon.*

The turning spoon also pulls outward on the twine and the twine pulls upward on the potato. The outward, or *centrifugal,* force acts through the string *on the potato*. There is no centrifugal force acting on the spoon.

The twirling spoon is similar to a satellite orbiting the earth. The one and only force acting on the satellite is a centripetal force. This inward force is supplied by the gravitational attraction of the earth.

Centrifugal force is exerted *by* the satellite *on* the earth. It is merely the gravitational attraction which the satellite holds for the earth.

The gravitational attraction of the earth for the satellite equals the attraction of the satellite for the earth, so that the centripetal and centrifugal forces equal one another. These two forces are oppositely directed: one acts on the earth, the other on the satellite.

In our experiment, if the centripetal force on the spoon is too little to keep the spoon in a circular orbit, the potato rises. It falls if the spoon's centripetal force is too great. Without the inward force on the spoon, the spoon would move off along a perfectly straight line. When the spoon moves too rapidly, the centripetal force pulls it in, but not enough to bring the spoon into a circular orbit. The potato rises as a result. On the other hand, if the spoon moves slowly, the cen-

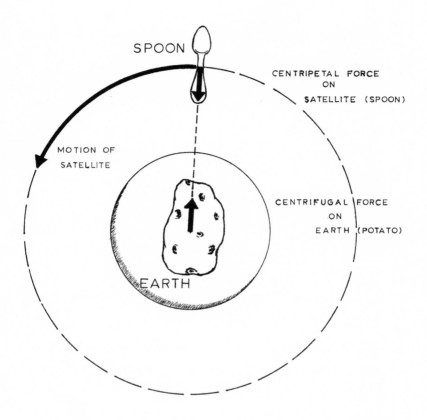

SPOON

CENTRIPETAL FORCE
ON
SATELLITE (SPOON)

MOTION OF
SATELLITE

CENTRIFUGAL FORCE
ON
EARTH (POTATO)

EARTH

tripetal force pulls the spoon even farther in than would be required for a circular orbit, and the potato falls.

Moons that orbit their planets and planets that orbit the sun behave in a similar fashion. If these move too fast or too slow they no longer move in a perfect circle. Instead, the moons or planets trace out elliptical—or oval—paths.

Whether an orbit is elliptical or circular, the

17

only force exerted on the orbiting object is an inward force. A continual inward pull is needed to turn a straight-line path into a circular or an elliptical one.

5 | Putting the "Fix" on a Wheel Race

A race is always good fun, whether it be a one-hundred-yard dash or a soap-box derby. In the name of science, you can run a "fixed" race—a race in which you will know the winner ahead of time.

The entries in the race will be two wheels, each exactly the same size and weight. The course, or track, will be an inclined plane. With a little knowledge of physics, you can see to it that one of the wheels always wins the race down the incline.

If you don't happen to have two identical wheels lying around the house, you can make some by taping two unbreakable dishes or saucers together, bottom to bottom. Now you must "fix" the con-

18

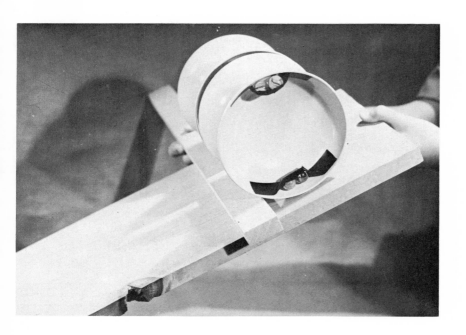

testing wheels by adding equal weights to each. To the first wheel add the weight at the very center; to the second wheel, add the weight close to the rim. If dishes or saucers are used, the weight of four marbles is sufficient. The rim-weighted wheel will roll smoothly if the weights are taped evenly on opposite edges of the wheel.

Any smooth board at least three feet long will serve as the track. Support one end on a box, and use a short stick placed across the track as a starting gate to insure a fair and even start.

19

A quick release of the stick and the race is on. Which wheel will win? You'll know the winner because you've rigged the race.

The wheel weighted at the center will win easily. Some of the energy of the slower wheel is used in spinning the rim weights around its own center. This means that there is less energy available to speed it down the inclined plane. There is no such problem with the faster wheel, which has its weights at the center.

If you can arrange to have the wheels go up a

slight incline again after coming down the track, notice what happens. The slower wheel will now gain on the faster one, as the stored energy in the spinning rim weights is used to move the wheel along. The two racers should go about the same distance up the slope.

If you ever plan to enter a soap-box derby, make sure the wheels of your racer have the least possible amount of weight near their rims.

6   Sweet Spot of the Bat

Every boy or girl who has ever swung a baseball bat knows that a bat has a sweet spot. A pitched ball hit near this spot on the bat will be a sweet hit. A ball hit too near the handle or too near the tip may sting your hands.

Baseball is an art—and a science. Get out your bat and let's learn a little of the science that's in it.

The sweet spot of a bat is the point that scien-

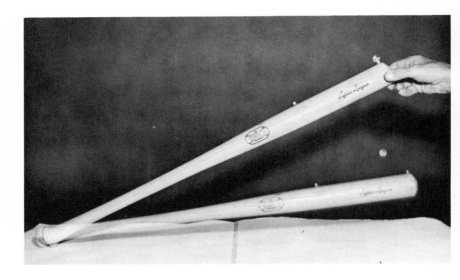

tists call the "center of percussion." This special point has some very interesting properties.

First, find a hard rubber or plastic mallet. Hold the handle of the bat between your thumb and forefinger. Now take the mallet and tap the bat lightly where you think the sweet spot should be. You may be surprised to feel a strong vibration in the bat. Tap the bat a little higher, then lower.

You will find a very special place on the bat. When the bat is struck at this place, there is no vibration. This is the sweet spot.

There is another experiment you can perform with the bat that is extremely interesting. We know that all freely falling objects fall at the same speed.

Let's drop a baseball to the ground. Will any object fall faster than the freely falling baseball? The answer is yes. The end of a bat will fall faster. Stand a bat on the ground, handle end down. Now let the tip fall. One special point on the bat will fall at the same speed as a freely falling object. You guessed it, this point is the center of percussion, the sweet spot of the bat.

If the center of percussion drops at the same speed as a ball released from the same height, all the parts of the bat nearer the handle must fall more slowly, and all the parts of the bat nearer the tip must fall faster.

Prove this to yourself by making a cup-shaped holder for a small marble that can be stuck to the tip end of the bat. With the bat at an angle, its handle resting on the ground, release the bat. You will be able to see the end of the bat falling away from beneath the marble. You will also hear a distinct click after the bat hits the ground when the marble lands a moment later.

Now move the marble holder toward the sweet spot. Again the click will be heard when the bat is dropped because the bat beats the marble to the ground. When the marble holder is placed at the sweet spot, however, the bat and marble will drop

23

at the same rate and there will be no click.

So next time you're up taking your cuts, remember the place on the bat that should connect with the ball—it is the sweet spot, of course.

7 ■ Tornado in a Smoke Ring

Let's blow some smoke rings. Nearly perfect smoke rings can be made with a coffee can or a round oatmeal box fitted with a rubber sheet on one end and a hole the size of a half dollar on the other.

The technical name for a smoke ring is "vortex ring" or "collar vortex." A vortex is any fluid which has a circular motion. Vortices are important in the fields of meteorology, aerodynamics, and hydrodynamics. Tornadoes are vortices, whirlpools are vortices, and the air behind the airfoils of an airplane or missile forms tiny vortices.

To make a smoke-ring generator first cut off the bottom of a coffee can. Fit a piece of cardboard in which you have cut a hole the size of a half dollar under the lip at the top of the can. If an oatmeal box is used, merely cut the hole in the bottom of the box. Now stretch the rubber from a large balloon over the other end and tie it tightly with a piece of string.

The generator must now be filled with smoke. The best smoke to use is made from a chemical called ammonium chloride. This perfectly harmless chemical comes in powder or tablet form and can be bought at any pharmacy.

Shape some aluminum foil around the bottom of a small bottle to make a container for the chemical. Place a pea-sized amount of the ammonium chloride inside the foil container. Now mold the top of the foil around a pencil to form a spout. Heat the chemical by holding the container over low heat on the kitchen stove. Take care not to burn yourself. Soon, dense white smoke will pour from the spout. Fill your smoke-ring generator through the hole.

Beautiful smoke rings are made simply by tapping the center of the rubber membrane. Out the hole they will shoot with each tap until the last bit of smoke inside the can is gone. Even after the smoke is gone, a tap on the membrane will produce a moving vortex ring. The smoke merely serves to make the vortex visible. In fact, vortex rings are formed whenever a fluid is given a quick localized motion.

Try knocking over some small paper or cardboard figures with vortex rings from your generator. Place the figures at a distance of four or five feet. The invisible vortex rings, or visible ones containing smoke, should do the job easily. Now stand at the same distance and try blowing the figures down. You may find this considerably more difficult, if not impossible.

Try tapping one smoke ring through the center of another. If your aim is just right, you will find that the ring coming up from behind will shrink temporarily, while the front ring will expand, as the second ring passes through.

Smoke rings remain in the form of a ring for such a long time because the only force which breaks them up is the friction of the air. If there were such a thing as a frictionless fluid, vortices could neither be created in this fluid, nor could they be destroyed if they were present in the first place. Because of this strange property, it was thought at one time that atoms were vortices in an imaginary fluid called "ether." The idea of a fric-

26

tionless "ether" that existed everywhere has been abandoned long ago, and with it, the concept of vortex atoms.

The study of the motion of fluids, and this includes both gases and liquids, remains today a very important one. Smoke rings have been with us a long time, but the nature and behavior of vortices are at present very important in the study of the flow of liquid fuel in rocket engines, the drag and

lift on the surface elements of aircraft, the heating of nose cones, and in the behavior of meteorological storms.

8 Whither the Whirl?

There is a widespread belief that water whirlpools down a washbowl drain counterclockwise in the Northern Hemisphere and clockwise in the Southern Hemisphere.

The water must spin this way, many people argue. Do not the cyclonic winds rushing into a low-pressure area spiral counterclockwise in the Northern Hemisphere, and clockwise in the Southern Hemisphere? Water running down a drain presents a similar situation, as the water rushes inward toward the opening like winds rushing in toward a low-pressure area.

Do you believe this washbowl story? The explanation certainly seems logical.

Test your washbowls at home to see if the water really does whirlpool away in a counterclockwise

28

direction. Test your tub drain too, and the kitchen sink as well.

What did you find? Didn't the water sometimes spiral out clockwise as well as in the expected counterclockwise way?

What's wrong with the beautiful theory that washbowl drains behave like cyclonic storms? One thing is wrong for sure. The people who believe this washbowl fantasy simply have never taken a good look at their own washbowls. A simple experiment can often correct in a few minutes a false idea that people have believed for years.

It is certainly true that basic laws of motion make cyclonic winds spiral the way they do. Any-

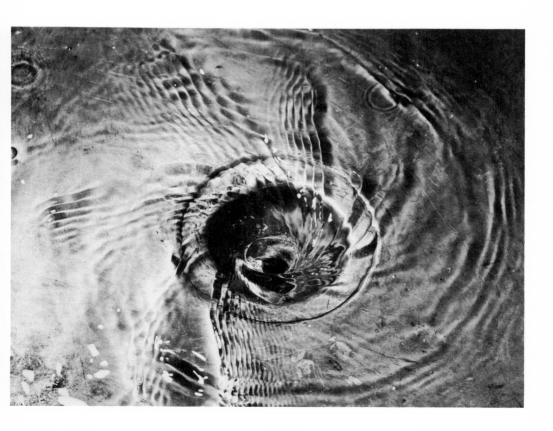

thing that moves over the surface of the earth curves to the right in the Northern Hemisphere and to the left in the Southern.

This effect is well known. It is called the Coriolis effect. It comes about because the earth on which we live is like a huge spinning merry-go-round. Motion appears to be different to a person riding on a merry-go-round than it does to a person standing on the ground. In the same way, motion observed by a person on the spinning earth appears to be different than the same motion seen by a person out in space.

The spin of the earth should also affect your washbowl drain—and it does. But its influence on the water is so small that it cannot be measured. Just as we know, for example, that the moon must exert a slight gravitational pull on our bodies in the moon's direction, but its influence is far too small to feel. We weigh the same when the moon is down as we do when it is high in the sky.

There are other influences, more immediate and far stronger than the Coriolis effect, which determine the whirlpooling direction of the water going down your drain. The shape of the drain opening, the shape of the bowl, the state of motion of the water before the plug is pulled, the way the drain is opened—all these determine whether the water drains out one way or the other.

So be careful, very careful. Even if an explanation for something sounds right, it may not be at all correct.

Coriolis effects, if not important in your washbowl, are extremely important in other situations. Consider the flight of an intercontinental ballistic missile. Suppose an ICBM is fired due north in the Northern Hemisphere. The Coriolis effect comes into play to curve it to the right. The missile will land east of the point from which it was fired. We cannot explain this in terms of the earth "spinning out from under" the missile, for we know the earth turns from west to east. This would lead us to believe that the ICBM would land to the *west* of the point from which it was fired.

A missile is observed to curve to the right in the Northern Hemisphere and to the left in the Southern Hemisphere only when its path is measured relative to the earth's surface. Since the earth's surface itself is not stationary, but moves, the "real" motion of the missile is difficult to observe directly.

The real motion is measured with respect to the stars. When motion is measured this way, Coriolis effects disappear. An object will not deflect either to the right or left unless some force acts in that direction.

9   What Makes Sammy Swim?

The sea horse is the only fish that swims in a vertical position. These little creatures do not swim very much, but Sammy the Sea Horse is an exception. He loves to swim—up and down, up and down. Mysteriously, he performs only at your command.

To make a swimming Sammy you will need a medicine dropper, which can be obtained at any drugstore. Be sure to get one with a narrow top. A quart soda-pop bottle with clear sides will serve well as an aquarium. You will also need a piece of Saran Wrap or the rubber from a balloon.

Fill the pop bottle with water to the very top. Draw a little water into the medicine dropper, enough so that it will just barely float. Place the

32

medicine dropper, rubber bulb at the top, in the bottle and cover the mouth tightly with the Saran Wrap or rubber.

Now press down firmly with your thumb. (If your thumb is large enough, you can dispense with the Saran Wrap or rubber altogether.) The medicine dropper should obediently descend to the bottom as you apply pressure to the mouth of the bottle. Release the pressure. The dropper should float back to the surface.

If you put too much water into the medicine dropper, it may not come back up. Too little water, and you will be unable to make it go down. A few trials will show how much water works best.

Now that you see what happens, you may wish to cut out a Sammy from sheet plastic or some other fairly stiff waterproof material and glue this onto the medicine dropper.

If you exercise a little cleverness, no one will be able to guess what you are doing to make Sammy swim.

Sammy's swimming isn't as mysterious as it may seem. The up-and-down motion can be explained by several basic physical principles.

Gases compress easily—large amounts can be squeezed into a small space. For example, a great

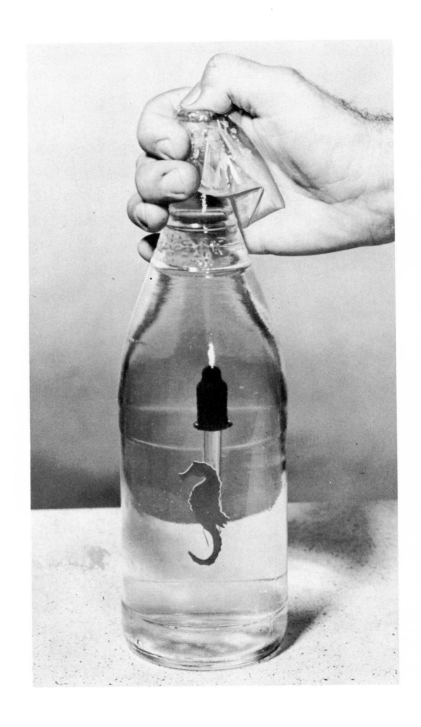

volume of air is pushed into bicycle or automobile tires. Liquids, on the other hand, are practically incompressible—you cannot force more water into a bottle which already is full. When you push down at the mouth of the pop bottle, this pressure is transmitted throughout the entire volume of water. The volume of the water, however, does not change.

But the air inside the medicine dropper can be compressed. Under pressure, its volume is reduced. When this occurs, a little extra water is shoved up into the dropper. Watch for this to happen as you apply pressure. The extra water makes the medicine dropper weigh a little more than it did before and it sinks to the bottom. When the pressure is removed, the compressed air inside the dropper pushes the water back to its original level. This reduces the weight and the dropper rises to the surface.

Notice that although you press your thumb down, the water inside the medicine dropper is forced up. This illustrates a fundamental principle about pressures in liquids: liquid pressure is exerted in all directions.

Be on the lookout for the pressure principle in action. You may find it where you least expect it.

10 Elastic Water

The surface of water behaves as if it were made of a thin film of rubber—rubber much like that in a toy balloon, but far more wonderful.

The elastic film on a water surface is water itself. Each drop from a faucet is enclosed in a bag of stretchy film, the water in a pan is covered by it, and a soap bubble is but a thin layer between two such films.

Satisfy yourself that elastic water surfaces really exist. Several interesting demonstrations will reveal their remarkable properties.

Secure a plastic berry or tomato box—the kind with open latticework. Place it gently on a surface of water. Magically, the box floats high and dry on top of the water. Here is a boat that has larger holes in its bottom and sides than it has solid places, yet the water is somehow kept from flowing through the holes and sinking the boat.

The box is suspended on the thin rubbery film which is the water surface. It does not float part way down in the water, like a cork, but rather glides about on top of an invisible elastic membrane.

Give the berry box a slight downward push. The water film is broken and the heavier-than-water container quickly sinks to the bottom.

Refloat the box. This time notice the pillow-shaped surface of water within each hole of the lattice. The elastic water layer stretches taut as it supports the weight of the box and the film protrudes slightly upward within the squares.

The elastic surface of water can also be shown to exert attractive and repulsive forces. Fill a drinking glass or cup nearly full with water. Float a small metal bottle cap upside down on the water surface. Notice that the cap is drawn toward the side of the glass. It is impossible to keep it floating in the center.

Now carefully add more water to the drinking glass until it is heaped up above the brim. (This in itself shows the power of the water film to keep the liquid from overflowing.) As this is done, the floating cap is suddenly repelled from the edge. It now stays in the center of the water surface, a place it previously avoided.

This peculiar behavior is caused by the stretchiness of the water film. A close look at the cap in the partly filled glass will reveal that the water is curved upward where it meets the cap and also at the sides of the tumbler. The two upward-curving portions of the film attract one another and the cap is pulled to the edge. When the glass is more than brimful, the water edge curves downward and repels the upward-curving film near the floating metal cap.

These demonstrations help us to understand the nature of liquid surfaces. How many other instances can you find where the elastic property of a liquid surface reveals itself?

11   Errant Crystal Atoms

Crystals are orderly arrangements of atoms, and this orderliness usually shows on the crystal surface. When we think of crystals, we usually think of beautiful gems, snowflakes, or such things as table salt and sugar. But in recent years scientists have learned to grow a greater variety of crystals than ever before. These synthetic crystals are extremely important in industry and in research.

Beautiful crystals can easily be grown at home in just a few minutes. To make your own crystals, get a small can or jar of Epsom salts (chemical name, magnesium sulfate). You may find some in your medicine cabinet or you can buy a small amount at the drugstore.

Heat half a cup of water on the stove. Add several teaspoons of Epsom salts to the water. Keep adding more salts to the water little by little until no more will dissolve. Now add several drops of

liquid household glue and while the mixture is
still warm, pour it onto a small piece of plate glass
and spread it evenly with a small cloth.

In a few minutes crystals will appear in the

liquid. These will grow before your eyes until the entire glass is covered with crystals as pretty as any you've seen on a frosty windowpane.

Except for the irregular places where they join, these crystals seem to be perfectly formed. Actually, however, individual crystals are never perfectly arranged. The tiny atoms of which they are formed—each no more than a hundred millionth of an inch in diameter—are not all in their proper places.

Physicists now realize that the really important feature of a crystal is not so much its perfection as its imperfection. A crystal can fall short of perfect orderliness in many ways. This may be for the best, as perfect crystals would be quite uninteresting.

Now let's make a model of a crystal. BB shot will serve well as our "atoms," although they are some ten million times greater in diameter than the real thing. You will also need a small tray to hold the shot. The under side of the lid from a quart or gallon paint can is ideal because it has a flat surface with no ridges or grooves. Three ten-cent packages of BB shot will more than cover a lid five inches in diameter.

Pour enough shot onto the lid or other small

tray to cover practically the entire surface. Immediately you will notice the tendency of the BB's to arrange themselves in a geometric fashion. If you gently shake the lid to and fro, and perhaps also rotate it back and forth, you will be able to align the shot in a nearly perfect array.

Notice that each BB is surrounded by six other BB's. This kind of arrangement is called "close packing," for the spheres in the single layer are as close together as they can be. (Close packing such as this is a typical arrangement of atoms in metals.) A real crystal contains many layers. Three layers would be required to surround any one atom or BB in the middle layer. In this case, the BB would have twelve, rather than six, nearest neighbors.

But here is the interesting part. Give the BB's a good mixing. Stir well. Then as you shake the tray gently you should notice several ways in which the arrangement of the shot falls short of the perfect orderliness you had previously.

Sometimes you will have atoms missing from their proper places in the BB crystal. This type of crystal defect is called a vacancy.

You will also have situations where the crystal arrangement may be perfect in one section of the lid, and perfect also in another, but the arrangement of atoms in one of these places doesn't jibe with the arrangement in the other. There is a disorganized boundary between the two regions. Atoms along the boundary don't quite belong to either of the adjacent regions of the crystal.

Here's something else to try. Shake the tray until a nearly perfect close-packed crystal arrangement is obtained. Take a single extra BB atom and push

it into the middle of the crystal. It shoves quite a few of the others to the side to make room for itself. Obvious defects show up in the crystal arrangement.

Now shake the tray again. The imperfection rapidly disappears. The extra atom itself has not moved to the crystal edge, but a number of other atoms have moved, each one a short distance. This realigns the crystal into good order.

You can also imagine a completely different kind of atom, or different size or color of BB, taking the place of one of the atoms in the crystal. This foreign atom represents a chemical impurity. This type of defect is responsible for the beautiful colors in certain gem stones.

12   Light Popper

Invisible "light" can be used to pop corn. This may seem a little strange, as we usually shake the corn popper over a stove or an open fire and let the flame do the job.

When one stops to think about it, popcorn ought to pop no matter how we heat it. A popper placed on the stove heats the corn by a process called conduction. First the flame or electric heating element heats the popper bottom, and this in turn heats the corn. All this is done by transferring heat by direct contact between the metal and hot gases.

But there is another way to heat corn. This is by

radiation. When we stand on a sunny ski slope on a cold day, we feel considerable heat that comes to us by direct radiation from the sun. The heat radiation from an infrared lamp can, in a similar way, heat the corn without warming the surroundings.

Let's try to pop corn with an infrared lamp. You may already have such a lamp at home. If not, you can purchase an inexpensive type of infrared bulb called a brooder lamp. Also find a set of embroidery hoops and enough cellophane to make two layers the size of the hoops. Clear or red cellophane is available as gift-wrapping material.

Place a single sheet of cellophane over the smaller embroidery hoop. Put a small amount of popcorn on the cellophane. Cover this with a second sheet of cellophane and stretch taut as you put the second hoop in place.

Now you are ready to pop the corn. Hold the cellophane sandwich as close to the infrared lamp as possible without touching it. Shake the hoops slightly so the corn will heat evenly. In a few minutes the corn will start to pop right in front of your eyes. Perhaps the popping is a more explosive affair than you had imagined.

Add salt and melted butter to the popcorn to make a small but tasty morsel.

If you felt the cellophane during the popping operation, you noticed that it became only slightly warm. The corn, on the other hand, became very hot—hot enough to be cooked. The cellophane didn't get hot enough to burn because most of the

48

infrared heat radiation passed right on through. It didn't pass through the corn. Here the heat rays were absorbed.

Infrared heat radiation is really a kind of light —a kind which is too "red" to be visible. Your infrared lamp gives off some visible light in addition to the infrared, but this visible light doesn't do the job of popping the corn. If you want to prove this to yourself, you can try holding the cellophane popper near an ordinary lamp to see what will happen.

Hold your hand near the infrared lamp. It warms up quickly. This is the action of the heat rays. A fluorescent lamp, on the other hand, gives off plenty of visible light, but very little heat radiation, as the hand test will quickly show.

13 Bucket Bass

A homemade bucket bass viol is capable of producing a fairly good musical tone. Aside from its musical qualities, it makes an excellent rhythm instrument.

Try making a musical bucket. You will learn something of the science of sound in the bargain.

The bucket part of the instrument can be any large tin can, two-quart pail, or even a strong cardboard box. The lid will not be needed. Make a hole for the instrument's single string by pounding a nail through the center of the bottom of the pail or can. Tie one end of a three-foot length of stout cord or string to a large button, and thread the cord up through the hole in the can. Tie another large button to the other end of the cord. Your bucket bass is now complete.

This instrument is easy to play. Seat yourself comfortably in a chair and wedge the can between your feet. Now hold the string taut with one hand by grasping the button on the end, and pluck the string with the other hand. You may be surprised to hear a full resonant tone.

You will notice that the pitch of the sound will vary with the tension you put on the cord. If you are not satisfied with the tone produced, try a different kind of string. Try also various cans or boxes. Perhaps a half-gallon ice-cream container or even a paper cup will give better tones.

50

The basic principle involved here is that vibrating objects produce sound. In this case the object is a piece of string. Other instruments may have a vibrating column of air, as in a trombone or pipe organ; still others contain vibrating solid objects, such as the reed in a clarinet and the wooden bars of a xylophone.

Many musical instruments utilize a partially enclosed space which amplifies the sound. The air in these cavities, and the walls as well, vibrate in resonance with the vibrator which originally produced the sound. For example, the richness of a violin's tone depends on its strings *and* on the beautiful sounding box; a mambo drum has an enclosed space beneath the membrane.

The can or box of your one-string instrument serves to amplify the sound, which otherwise would be quite thin and weak. As the string vibrates back and forth, the bucket or box bottom holding the string vibrates in and out. In turn, the enclosed air vibrates, amplifying the sound.

14 Dancers on a Gong

One of the liveliest dances you've ever seen can be held on a ballroom floor made from the lid of a fry pan. It's not rock 'n' roll, and certainly not a waltz. It's rather like a wild and primitive ceremonial rite.

The dancers will be grains of salt. These crystals of salt cannot get out of step, for their rhythm is provided by a vibrating dance floor. A queer way to dance—but let's see what it's all about.

Sounds are infinite in variety. Some are sweet, some are sour. Others are harsh, booming, shrill, brassy, resonant. The list is endless. The sound of a gong is pleasant. Let's make one, and then try the wild dance on its surface.

The lid of a large fry pan makes an excellent gong. One whose metal is not too thick works best. It can be either squarish or round. A round metal

serving tray often makes a good vibrant tone. There is a little trick in getting a musical sound from such objects, so you may have to experiment a bit to find the best way.

A dead metallic sound is produced when the lid or tray is held in the hand. To get a musical tone, the object must be free to vibrate. Test various lids and trays you find around the house for their musical quality by suspending them from a string and striking them with a small mallet made from a pencil stuck into a hard rubber eraser.

Find a lid that gives a full resonant sound and from which the handle can be removed and later replaced. Mount it horizontally on the top of a stick with a few layers of felt between the lid and stick. Next, put a small screw through the hole in the lid and fasten it loosely to the stick. Make sure the lid has plenty of play.

Sprinkle some table salt evenly over the top of the lid, and strike it in the place that gave the deepest resonant sound. Watch carefully. The salt will dance violently at certain places on the lid. At other places, the salt will remain perfectly motionless.

The dancing salt shows where the lid vibrates. The still salt shows where it does not. The dancers form a pattern as in a square dance, a pattern

54

which is determined by the shape of the lid and the point at which it is struck. A square lid should give two distinct patterns, one pattern from a blow at the corner, and another from a tap at the center of one side.

If your lid slopes toward the edges, the vibrating salt will dance off the sides and will leave a pattern on the lid which shows the non-vibrating part of the gong very clearly.

Vibrations of objects produce sound. A plucked string is perhaps the simplest vibrating object. The fry pan-lid gong, like a drum, is a more complicated affair. Somewhere in every musical instrument, and in any other object that gives off sound of any kind, a vibration takes place to produce the sound.

15   Pinhole Camera

Very good photographs can be taken with a simple pinhole camera that you can make yourself. A pinhole camera has a pinhole instead of a lens.

Science uses the art of photography in many ways. You can learn many of the basic principles of this art with a pinhole camera and have a lot of fun as well.

A pinhole camera should not be thought of as an inferior instrument. Although exposure times must be relatively long because of the small hole through which the light must go, the image on the film is entirely free from distortions common to many lenses. Another advantage is that the camera is always in focus for objects both near and far.

To construct a pinhole camera, we must first make a perfectly light-tight cardboard box. A snugly fitting outer box will enclose an inner box open at both ends. A box six or so inches long is a good size. The outer box should be in two parts, one half fitting on from the front, the second half from the rear.

Make some heavy cardboard strips to be located just inside the rear of the inner box. The film will fit against these strips and be held in place by a thick piece of cardboard the same size as the film.

This film recess must be made the proper size. Sheet film 2 1/4 by 3 1/4 inches is fairly economical. Roll film is cheaper, but you will need complete darkness when you cut it in strips of the proper length to fit your camera.

Now make a hole about the size of a dime in the center of the front of the camera box. A small piece of aluminum foil is to be taped over this hole. First a pinhole of the proper size must be made in the foil. The best hole size depends on the length of your box from the pinhole to the film. A common household straight pin is 0.029 inch in diameter. This makes a hole of the proper size for a box about a foot long. Since you will want a box about half this long, a smaller hole is best, one about 0.020 inch in diameter. A very small needle is about this size. Check to see that the needle is about two-thirds as thick as an ordinary pin.

Make sure your box is light-tight before you attach the foil with the pinhole. Hold the box near a bright light and peer into the dime-sized hole. If any light is seen, you must eliminate its cause. When you are sure your camera box is light-tight, tape on the foil so that the pinhole is in the center of the front end of the box. You will also need a cover over the pinhole that can act as a shutter. A small piece of cardboard held in place with a rubber band will do. Another light-tight box will be needed to store exposed film. Again, a box-within-a-box is best for this.

On the top and side of the box draw lines from the position of the pinhole to the corners of the film position. Any object in front of the camera which lies within the extension of these lines will appear in your picture.

Now you are ready to load the camera with film. Find a dark closet for this operation, as you will have to insert and remove film from your camera in total darkness unless you obtain the proper

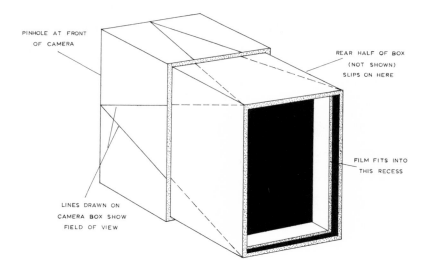

PINHOLE AT FRONT
OF CAMERA

REAR HALF OF BOX
(NOT SHOWN)
SLIPS ON HERE

FILM FITS INTO
THIS RECESS

LINES DRAWN ON
CAMERA BOX SHOW
FIELD OF VIEW

safelight for the film you are using. Remove a sheet of film from its package, being careful to handle it only at the edges. Moisten your lips and place one edge of the film between them. The side that sticks to your lip carries the photographic emulsion. This side must be placed toward the pinhole. Now place the cardboard sheet behind the film and slip the rear half of the outer box over the back of the camera.

All set? Then let's shoot some pictures. It will be best to photograph only outdoor scenes and still life, as it is doubtful that any of your friends could hold still long enough to have their pictures taken. Find some solid object on which to rest your cam-

59

era so that it doesn't move while the picture is being taken. Through practice you will learn to spot the shots that will make attractive and interesting pictures.

In bright sunlight try an exposure time of about twenty seconds for film with a daylight "speed" of about 50. The speed of a film, an index to its sensitivity to light, is indicated on the package. If you get film with a speed rating of 100, the exposure time can be cut to ten seconds. The proper exposure will depend on many things: the size of the pinhole, the kind of film, and the amount of light on your subject. Shoot several pictures using your best estimate of the proper exposure time. Then photograph these same scenes using exposure times both half as long and twice as long as you used originally. Keep a list of your subjects and exposure times and get these pictures developed before taking more. From your results you can decide the best exposure times to use.

You may wish to try developing your own pictures. If you do, supplies and instructions are available at any photographic supply store.

16   Moiré Shadow Patterns

You can see them in many places—in the folds of marquisette curtains, in the window reflection of matchstick bamboo drapes, in picket fences and wrought-iron railings, in organdy dresses, and occasionally, on the television screen.

What can you see? Moiré shadow patterns. You have undoubtedly *seen* them, but have you really *observed* them? There is an important distinction here.

Scientists, and others, should be able to do more than merely see, they should be able to observe.

Moiré (pronounced mwah-ray′) patterns are formed by the interference between two similar geometrical patterns. The name originally referred to the pattern seen in watered silk and other watered fabrics.

To learn more about these most interesting shadow patterns, find two small pieces of semitransparent ribbed fabric. Test the fabric for its moiré pattern. To do this, fold the material double with the ribbing of the two pieces running nearly parallel. Look through the fabric sandwich at the sky or a bright light. Hold one piece still and turn the other one slightly until the moiré shadows appear—a whole set of them in parallel lines. Here is the surprising part. The moiré pattern lies perpendicular to the ribbing in the material.

Once you have found a material that shows the pattern clearly, it will be best to mount the two pieces in separate holders. Two small embroidery holders will serve well.

Place the two holders together, fabric against fabric. Find the moiré pattern again by rotating one of the holders until the weave in the two pieces of fabric is nearly aligned. Notice what happens when one of the holders is rotated slightly. The moiré shadows become more closely spaced as the angle between the ribbing in the two pieces of fabric is increased. If the ribbing is made to line up exactly, the moiré pattern becomes very irregular and the shadows widely spaced. This irregularity comes from the irregularity in the weave of the fabric itself or from the mounting. If the threads in both pieces of material were perfectly straight, the fabric sand-

wich would show no shadow bands. The pattern would be all shadow, all light, or something in between.

Perhaps you can now guess that the shadows in the moiré pattern are formed by the points of intersection of the more opaque parts of the weave. The fabric acts as if it were a set of parallel dark strips. When two such patterns overlap at a slight angle, the intersection of the strips forms bands of shadow at right angles to the strips themselves. Convince yourself that this is true by drawing two sets of lines on paper to represent the ribs in the fabric. Hold them, sandwiched, to the light and you will see that the greater the angle between the two sets of strips, the smaller the spacing between successive shadow lines.

A moiré pattern is formed whenever two similar geometrical patterns overlap. Television interference often comes in the form of a regular pattern that "overlaps" the horizontal parallel sweeps of the spot which makes the picture. A moiré pattern is formed when this happens. Moiré patterns are formed in curtain material when two portions of the fabric overlap. The same is true in an organdy dress. Picket-fence effects come in when one fence is viewed through another. A fence and its shadow can also form a moiré pattern, as can a matchstick bamboo curtain and its reflection in the window. There are many other examples of this effect. How many can you find?

Moiré patterns are more than an interesting novelty. They have proved extremely useful in making accurate measurements of angles and distances. Move one of your fabric holders slowly across the other in a direction parallel to the lines of the moiré pattern. What happens? The shadow lines move at right angles to the motion of the fabric, and, at a much greater speed. The motion of the moiré shadows provides a kind of magnified view of the motion of the fabric. A large number of shadows go by when one holder with its fabric is moved an inch. This splits the inch into many divisions for accurate measurement. Of course fabric is not used for these more accurate measurements, but special grids made for the purpose. The counting of the shadows is done automatically by photoelectric cells.

Perhaps you can make a calipers that works on this principle. With it you can measure small distances quite accurately.

17 Pin Optics

A few ordinary straight pins, a sheet of paper, piece of cardboard, protractor, ruler, pencil, and mirror are all the pieces of equipment you will need to en-

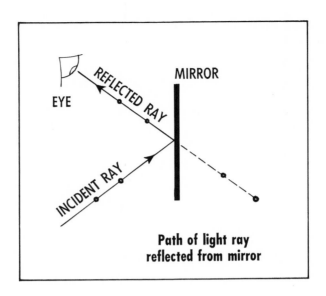

**Path of light ray
reflected from mirror**

gage in that old and hallowed form of experimentation called "Pin Optics."

The pins are used to mark the paths of light rays.
Any two pins stuck in the cardboard mark a
straight line running through the pins. They also
mark the path of a single light ray moving in line
with the pins. Light rays traced in this way can
show us how certain optical systems work.

Let's explore the workings of a simple flat mirror. It forms an image behind the mirror of any
object placed in front. What actually happens to
light rays that bounce off the mirror? And why is
an image that really isn't there formed behind the
mirror?

66

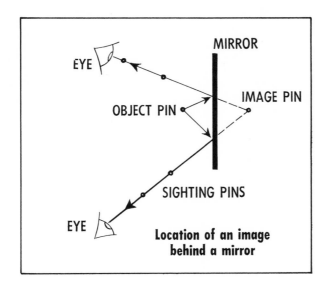

EYE

MIRROR

OBJECT PIN

IMAGE PIN

SIGHTING PINS

EYE

**Location of an image
behind a mirror**

To find out, prop a pocket mirror up against a small block of wood, or better yet, glue it to the side of the block. Put a sheet of paper on top of some heavy cardboard and place the mirror on the paper. Now stick two pins in front of the mirror so that the straight line connecting the two makes an angle—any angle—with the mirror.

Looking in the mirror you will see the images of the two pins. Now stick two more pins into the paper so that they line up exactly with the two image-pins seen in the mirror. The first two pins mark the path of a light ray striking the mirror; the second two pins mark the path of this same light ray after reflecting in the mirror.

Draw a line along the back edge of the mirror to mark its position on the paper. Remove the pins and draw a straight line with a ruler through each pair of pin pricks. These lines show the path of a single light ray that bounced off the mirror. Using a protractor, measure the angle each of these lines makes with a line perpendicular to the surface of the mirror. You should find that these two angles are equal. This will be true for every angle which a ray of light might make with the mirrored surface.

You have just confirmed the law of reflection. This law states that the angle of incidence (the angle the ray makes as it strikes the surface of a mirror) equals the angle of reflection (for the same ray bouncing off).

Now let's find the precise position of an image in the mirror. Place a single pin in front of the mirror. This we will call the object-pin. Immediately, its companion—the image-pin—comes into view "behind" the mirror. Place two more pins out front so that they are in line with the image-pin. The image-pin must now be located somewhere on the straight line formed by these two real pins. But we haven't yet quite located the image-pin since it could be anywhere along this line. Let's repeat

68

this procedure with two more pins that make a different angle with the mirror. The image-pin must also be located somewhere on the line formed by the second pair of pins.

If the image-pin is located somewhere on the first straight line and also somewhere on the second, the only place it can be is at the intersection of these two lines.

Mark the mirror position as before and remove the two pairs of sighting pins. Draw a straight line through each pair of pin pricks. The image-pin must be located at their intersection.

Measure the perpendicular distance from the mirror to the object-pin. Measure also the distance from the mirror to the image of this pin. You

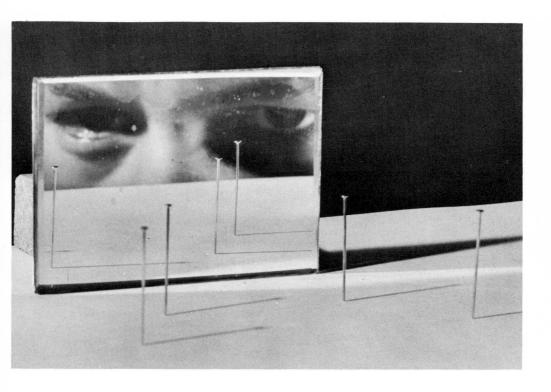

should find that these two distances are the same.

You have shown that a mirror image is to be found as far behind the mirror surface as the object is in front. This is true for each and every point on any object and its corresponding image in the mirror.

As a last step, draw straight lines between the object-pin and the points where the two straight lines to the image cross the mirror surface. These lines, together with the lines previously drawn in front of the mirror, mark the paths of two rays that leave the object-pin and reflect from the mirror. As you can easily see, it is these reflected rays that make light appear to come from an imaginary pin located behind the mirror surface.

18 Mirror Multiplication

Would you like to double, triple, or even quadruple your money? It is easily done. Unfortunately, none of this increased wealth can ever be spent.

This money magic can be performed with two ordinary pocket mirrors. Glue or tape a small block of wood to the back of each mirror so they can be set up vertically on a table.

Place the two mirrors at right angles, their edges touching. Place a coin between them. Instead of a single coin, you now have four. When an object is placed in front of a single mirror, the object and a single image in the mirror are seen. With the double mirror, not one, but three images are seen.

Try changing the angle between the mirrors. Positions will be found giving two, three, four, five, or more images.

Even King Midas wouldn't be able to count all the coins that can be seen when the two mirrors are placed several inches apart, parallel, and facing each other. To see this great wealth, place a coin between the mirrors and look past the back edge of one mirror into the other.

Some of the great palaces in Europe have rooms with mirror-covered walls opposite one another. In the palace mirrors a person can see countless images of himself that extend in single file off into the distance.

Something very special happens when two mirrors are positioned to form a right-angle corner,

like adjacent walls of a room. This is the arrangement that produced three coin images. Find a small paper with some writing on it, a watch, or any other object whose left and right sides can be distinguished. Place this in a vertical position in front of the corner mirror. The middle image, the one seen along the edge between the two mirrors, appears exactly the same as the object viewed directly.

If you think this is not at all strange, place the same object in front of a single mirror. This time everything is reversed, left for right and right for left. Printing is difficult if not impossible to read. The hands of a watch move the wrong way. The image you see of yourself in a mirror is not the same image as others see of you. If you are right-handed, your mirror image is left-handed. Wink your left eye, and your image winks his right. In a corner mirror, however, all this is changed. One image is identical to the object. You then see yourself exactly as others see you.

Twin mirrors provide an excellent way of dividing a circle into equal parts. Adjust the angle between the two mirrors so that a number of whole images are seen—no partial sections of an image should be visible. Now count all the images and add one for the object itself. This number divided into the 360 degrees of a complete circle gives the angle between the mirrors. To illustrate, when the total number of images seen is five and one is added for the object itself to make six, the angle between

the mirrors must be 360 degrees divided by six, or 60 degrees.

The mirrors multiply the way they do because light can bounce from them in a variety of ways. When the angle between the mirrors is small, light from the object is reflected back and forth between the mirrors a number of times before it enters your eye. Each possible combination of reflections produces its own image. As the angle is reduced, additional reflection combinations increase the number of images. This continues until the mirrors are parallel, when we no longer can count the images trailing off in both directions.

19 There Was a Crooked House

You can see how handsome you look in a round, shiny Christmas-tree ornament—your beautiful nose is about five times its normal size, your mouth could swallow a grapefruit easily, and your head

74

seems to come to a lovely mountain peak. In all fairness, your image in the shiny bulb really doesn't do you justice. The bulb greatly distorts your facial features.

Borrow a shiny, perfectly round bulb from your Christmas trimmings to perform a little experiment. A silver-colored one will be best, although any other light color will do. The object of the experiment is to find out how the spherical bulb distorts the images seen in it.

If you have a checkerboard, place the ornament on it and look at the checkerboard image in the bulb. Put one row of squares in line with your eye and the bulb. You can also use a sheet of ruled notebook paper. Place the paper first with the rulings running toward the bulb, then with the lines running crossways.

Notice that the parallel lines which run toward the ornament form curved image lines in the globe which fan apart markedly. The image of a line which is farther away from the bulb is not nearly so distorted as the image of a line closer to the bulb.

Lines that run crossways to your line of sight become highly curved when viewed in your optical ornament. Instead of showing as straight and horizontal parallel lines, they curve up on either side. Again we see that the lines close to the bulb give more highly curved images than those farther away.

Here is the most interesting part of the experiment. It is possible to draw a distorted object on the paper which will appear perfectly straight and true when its image is viewed in the ornament. What you want is a drawing which is already distorted in such a way that the distorting action of the reflecting bulb will cancel it out.

Place the ornament on a clean sheet of paper. Draw any picture you wish. But instead of looking at the paper, make the drawing watching the image in the ornament. When you are finished, you will find that, when viewed directly, the drawing you've made on the paper looks pretty silly.

In the accompanying photograph, the image in the Christmas tree ornament shows a simple house with reasonably straight sides and a normal roof and chimney. But the drawing that makes this image shows an extremely crooked and curvy house. A normal-looking home drawn on the paper, on the other hand, will produce a very curvy image-home.

Now let your imagination run loose. How many

different kinds of objects can you draw that will appear proper and normal when viewed in the ornament but are completely distorted in the drawing?

What you've done here is really very similar to

the way in which an optical designer goes about his work. A single lens in a camera, microscope, pair of binoculars, or a telescope, often produces an image which is distorted. Other lenses or mirrors are then designed which "undistort" the image. In other words, it doesn't matter if one lens or mirror makes an inaccurate image so long as other optical elements undo the previous distortions with new distortions of their own.

This is why cameras often contain three or more lenses instead of one, why telescope lenses are never single but contain at least two lenses close together, and why microscopes often contain many lenses in addition to those in the eyepiece.

20   Magnify It

Three or four identical ten-cent lenses can be easily arranged in various ways to make a compound magnifier, a microscope, and a telescope.

Secure two cardboard tubes, one from a roll of

toilet tissue and one from a roll of waxed paper or aluminum foil. Lenses that will fit inside these cardboard tubes are available at most dime stores and toy counters.

Optical lenses are used in a wide variety of instruments. They are to be found in cameras, eyeglasses, surveyors' transits, periscopes, and movie projectors, as well as in magnifiers, microscopes, and telescopes. Many of the basic principles involved in these instruments can be demonstrated with the simple lenses used in these experiments.

Observe first the action of a single lens. Hold a lens five to ten feet from a window inside the house. Hold up a sheet of white paper behind the lens. Adjust the distance between the lens and the paper until a sharp image of the scene outside the window shows clearly on the paper. Notice that the image on the paper not only is upside down but also is reversed right to left.

The distance between the lens and the image of a distant object is called the focal length of the lens. The single lens used in this way is working exactly as the lens in a camera. In a camera, film in a light-tight box is put in the same position as the white paper.

Hold the lens in front of an object which is closer

than the scene outside the window. You will find that the distance between the lens and paper will have to be increased if a sharp image is to be formed on the paper.

A single lens can be used as a simple magnifying glass. Hold the lens an inch or two from the print in this book. Now, keeping your eye about a foot away, adjust the position of the lens until a clear image is obtained. The print is seen right side up and magnified. Now place two of the lenses together. This time the magnification is about twice as great because two lenses together are stronger than a single lens. If you make a focal-length measurement for the pair of lenses placed together, you will find a value half as large as that found for a single lens.

A better magnifier can be made by placing a lens at each end of a cardboard tube from a roll of toilet tissue. The two lenses should be separated by a distance of about half the focal length of one of the lenses. Notice that with this magnifier, the image is not so distorted at the edges as the image produced by a single lens, nor is it so likely to show blue and orange-red edges on the images of the black letters.

A compound microscope is the next instrument

to make. This is made with a strong lens near the object to be viewed and a weaker lens next to the eye. Fit two of your lenses into one end of the cardboard tube from a roll of waxed paper or alumi-

num foil. Fit a third lens into the end of your shorter tube. This short tube should slide in and out of the longer tube to allow you to make necessary adjustments. The single lens will act as the eyepiece of the microscope.

The distance between the two-lens end of the microscope and the object to be viewed must be varied until the upside-down image as seen through the single lens comes into focus. If you have a fourth lens, add it to the pair to produce greater magnification.

A telescope is similar to a microscope except that it is used for viewing objects that are far away rather than tiny ones near at hand. To make your telescope, merely turn the microscope around so that the two-lens combination is next to your eye. Since the distance from the lens to the object viewed cannot be changed very much, the proper adjustment of the distance from the two lenses next to your eye to the single lens at the far end of the tube is important.

Look through the telescope with one eye at a window or other rectangular object, and with your other eye look directly at the object. You will find that this is a two-power telescope, for the telescope image appears twice as large as the object viewed directly. Placing three lenses in the eyepiece will provide a magnification of three.

As with the microscope, the telescope image will be upside down. Astronomical telescopes also show things upside down. But astronomers do not mind this, since an upside-down star looks pretty much the same as one right-side up. A telescope that shows things right-side up requires special prisms or extra lenses.

21 Blow Bubble Colors

Most everyone is familiar with the myriad colors shown by soap bubbles. Did you ever wonder how these beautiful colors are produced? As with so many of the wonders of nature, such things are usually taken for granted.

Blow some soap bubbles—but this time take a really good look at them. The special soap-bubble mix available at toy counters and ten-cent stores is the easiest to use. Carefully examine a large bubble

near a bare light bulb. You'll probably see several things you never noticed before.

As soon as the bubble is formed, nearly every color of the rainbow can be seen swimming about in the soap film. The brilliant rainbow colors can be seen best by looking at the bright image of the

84

light bulb showing in the bubble. After a short time, a close look will reveal a series of horizontal colored bands near the bottom of the bubble. At the top of the bubble the bright colors will turn a ghostly gray just before the bubble bursts.

The bands of color are formed by a process called interference. The outside and inside surfaces of the soap film are like two walls. Light bounces back and forth many times inside the film of soap solution between these two walls. Each time the light strikes a surface of the film, some of the light goes on through, some reflects. The color of the light coming through the film will be strong and bright if all the light rays of that particular color are "in step" with one another as they come out of the bubble. This color will be suppressed completely if the emerging light rays are "out of step" with each other.

White light is in this way broken up to give blue bands wherever the thickness of the soap film is just right to make the emerging blue rays of light fall "in step." Red bands are formed wherever the film thickness causes emerging red rays to be "in step," and so on.

Two different colors are never in step at the same place on the bubble because the "steps" of one color are a different size than the "steps" of another. Red steps are relatively long ones; violet steps are the shortest. The "step" length of a particular color is called its wave length.

Bubble colors in this way provide a kind of thickness map of the bubble. At one red band, for example, the bubble is slightly thicker than at the adjacent yellow band. It is also just one red "step" thicker or thinner than the thickness of the bubble film at the next red band.

The horizontal rows of color sometimes seen near the bottom of the bubble are produced when the soap film thickens there. The gray color seen at the top is perhaps the most interesting feature of the bubble. Gray is produced when the soap film becomes so thin that every color interferes with itself and all rays fall out of step. No clear colors can emerge. The gray soap film is less than six millionths of an inch thick.

22   Compass Paradox

The north end of the needle of a magnetic compass has a magnetism which is the same as that found at the south magnetic pole. The south end of the compass needle is like the north magnetic pole.

It would seem that north is south, and south is north. Confused? Then let's get this awkward situation straightened out.

As a start, secure an inexpensive compass and a horseshoe or bar magnet from the dime store or hobby shop. You may be lucky enough to find a more powerful magnet from an old radio loudspeaker, an auto speedometer, or telephone receiver. The compass needle is itself a tiny magnet, so you will actually have two magnets with which to experiment.

Bring one end of the magnet near the compass. You will find that one side of the horseshoe (or one end of the bar magnet) will attract the point of the compass needle and repel the tail of the needle. The opposite end of the magnet will attract the tail of the compass needle and repel the point.

The compass needle can be led around in circles like a puppy on a leash. The "leash" is an invisible force acting between the two magnets. This attraction and repulsion of magnets are usually summed up in the statement: Like poles (ends) repel, unlike poles attract.

Here is a way of naming the two ends of a magnet to keep them straight in your mind. Forget the labels "north" and "south" because these lead to confusion with North and South on the earth's surface. Call the end of the compass needle that points north the "North Seeking" (NS) end of the tiny magnet, the opposite end the "South Seeking" (SS) end. Now the NS and SS ends of any magnet can be identified through their influence on the compass needle.

Opposite poles attract one another. The kind of magnetism found near the north magnetic pole attracts the NS end of the compass needle and must therefore be SS magnetism. That found near the south magnetic pole must be NS.

Try making your own magnetic compass. You will need a large sewing needle, a cork or other

float, and a tumbler full of water. The sewing needle will be your pointer, but first it must be magnetized. Stroke it from its center to one end with one side of the horseshoe magnet. With the other side of the magnet, stroke the needle from its center to the opposite end. A dozen strokes or so should do the job. The sewing needle may now be tested for its magnetism by watching its influence on the magnetic compass.

Place the magnetized sewing needle on a cork or pop-bottle cap floating in a tumbler brimful of water. This provides a nearly frictionless bearing for the swinging of the sewing needle. The cork will stay away from the sides of the tumbler if the water in the tumbler is heaped slightly above the edge.

The magnetic sewing needle will align itself with the earth's magnetism, the NS end of the needle pointing north. Notice that your homemade compass does not point to true geographic north. The geographic north and south poles are determined by the axis of spin of the earth. The compass points instead to the north magnetic pole. This is a spot in the northern extremes of Canada at latitude 73 degrees north and longitude 100 degrees west. The deviation of the compass needle from true north varies from point to point over the face of the earth.

23 Electricity and Magnets on the Move

An electric current produces magnetism, and moving magnetism produces an electric current. Since an electric current consists of moving electric charges, the *motion* of electric charges and the *motion* of magnetism are intimately related. Let's perform some experiments with both electricity and magnets on the move.

First, let's make a magnet with moving electric charges. An ordinary bar or horseshoe magnet owes its magnetism to moving charges. In such a magnet, electric charges within the metal continually spin around in tiny atom-sized circles. Our magnet will be made by an electric current that moves through a wire in much larger loops. It will be an electromagnet.

Secure a large nail, a couple of flashlight batteries, and about ten feet of bell wire. Bell wire can be obtained at any hardware store or hobby shop. Wind the wire in tight turns around the length of the nail. Make three layers, taking care to wind the wire in one direction only. Leave about a foot of the wire at each end to make the leads to the batteries. A little tape at each end of the coil on the nail will keep the wire from unwinding.

Tape the two flashlight cells together tightly, the bottom of one on the top of the other. Scrape the insulation from the two ends of the wire and tape one of them to the bottom of the lower battery.

Your electromagnet is now complete. When the free wire is touched to the top of the batteries, the electrical circuit is closed. The nail with its coil of wire becomes a powerful magnet. Test it for its ability to pick up small objects containing iron. When the circuit is opened, the flow of electric charges in the loops of wire stops and the magnetism disappears.

This completes the first experiment. Moving electricity makes a magnet, and when the electric charges stop flowing, the magnetism is no more.

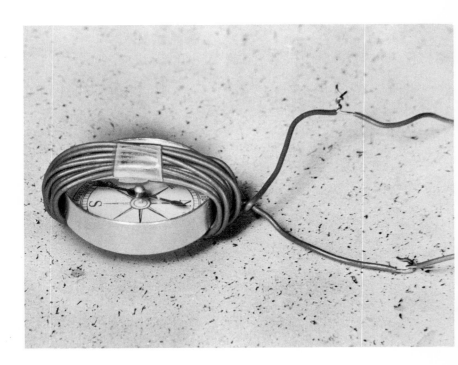

Now we shall see that a moving magnet can produce an electric current. This experiment was first performed by Michael Faraday in England in 1831. It is worth repeating. You will need a small magnetic compass, a toy magnet, about twenty-five feet of bell wire, and a single flashlight cell.

Before producing an electric current with moving magnetism, we must make an instrument for detecting the presence of this current. A small magnetic compass will do this nicely if a neat coil

of about twenty turns of bell wire is made across one diameter of the compass. Leave six inches free at each end of the wire. Turn the compass so that the needle lines up with the coil. You now have a very sensitive current-detecting device called a galvanometer.

Prove that the galvanometer really does detect the presence of an electric current. Scrape the insulation from the two free ends of the coiled wire and touch them to the top and bottom of a small flashlight battery. The compass needle will violently turn and point crossways to the coil windings. The galvanometer works because moving electric charges make a magnet. The magnetism of the coil around the compass has a stronger influence on the needle than the magnetic pull of the earth. Because of this, the compass needle "lines up" with this new magnetism. When the current through the coil is stopped, the compass needle returns to its alignment with the weaker magnetism of the earth.

Now make another coil of bell wire by wrapping thirty or more turns of wire into a loop several inches in diameter. The ends of the wire to this coil should be left at least two feet long. Tape the coil so that it will stay together.

We are now ready to produce an electric current

with a moving magnet. Connect the long leads of the second coil to the galvanometer coil. If an electric current can be produced in the second coil, the current will also flow through the galvanometer coil and cause a deflection in the compass needle.

Quickly thrust a magnet through the coil. As you do this, carefully observe the needle of the galvanometer. It will swing to one side as the magnet moves in and will return to its original position when the magnet stops moving. The long leads on the large coil prevent the moving magnet from having a direct effect on the compass needle. Now quickly withdraw the magnet from the coil. The galvanometer needle will move in a direction opposite to its original deflection.

Since the galvanometer deflects only when the bar magnet is thrust into the coil and when it is removed, there must be an electric current that is generated within the coil only during these times. This is it. This is the result we were looking for. A moving magnet can produce an electric current, and this current is generated in the large coil.

The generation of an electric current in a coil by a moving magnet is one of the most fundamental and important properties in the entire field of electricity. Most electric power production is based on this principle.

The intimate relationship between electricity and magnetism is well illustrated by Faraday's experiment with the moving magnet. An electric current produces magnetism, and conversely, moving magnetism produces an electric current.

24 Wire a Telegraph Buzzer

Electricity is our most versatile worker. It can be made to perform countless chores. It may operate a gigantic electronic computer or grind up garbage in the kitchen sink.

A telegraph buzzer is easily made and illustrates how effortlessly an electric current can be made to behave as directed. In this case, it turns itself off and on many times a second. The telegraph will enable you—once you learn the Morse code—to send messages to someone across the room, down in the basement, or even next door.

You will need some scraps of wood and metal, a few wood screws, a brass machine screw with two

nuts, a bolt or nail, a six-volt battery, about twenty feet of bell wire, and a springy length of metal such as a length of clock spring. In place of the clock spring, a nail file, kitchen spatula, or even a putty knife may be used.

A strong electromagnet must be made first. Mount a heavy nail, or preferably a bolt with a nut on the end, through the bottom of a small piece of scrap wood as shown in the accompanying photograph. Wrap three or four layers of bell wire around the bolt along its full length, leaving a foot or more of wire free at both ends. If you do not have a nut to fit the top of the bolt, be sure to tape the wire, so that it will not come loose.

Now mount a three- or four-inch length of a softened clock spring (or nail file, spatula, or putty knife) so that it clears the top of the bolt by about 1/32 inch and extends an inch or more beyond the bolt. The clock spring is softened by heating it red hot and allowing it to cool slowly. Whatever metal is used must be mostly iron. In case this metal cannot be drilled, fix it in place with two wood screws, one on either side of the metal strip.

A short length of stiff metal is next mounted above the end of the clock spring. Place a small brass machine screw on this strip with a nut on both sides so that the screw may be locked securely in place. Round the bottom of the machine screw with a file and adjust the screw so that it will touch the clock spring.

The last thing you will need to make is a telegraph key. A short length of sheet metal about the thickness of the metal in a tin can will be needed. Screw one end of this strip to a small wooden base. Mount another wood screw underneath the opposite end of the strip.

Now wire the battery, the telegraph key, and the buzzer together as shown in the photograph. Strip the insulation from the ends of the wire and tighten firmly under each screw. Although two flashlight

98

cells may be used to operate the buzzer, a six-volt lantern battery provides much more positive action.

When the key is depressed and touches the screw, the circuit is closed. Electric current flows through the coil, putting the electromagnet into action. This pulls the clock spring toward the electromagnet. But as it does this, the clock spring is also pulled away from the screw contact point. This opens the circuit, the electromagnet loses its pull, and the clock spring springs back to its original position. Now the circuit is closed again and the electromagnet goes into action once more. Once again the circuit is opened. This sequence of events occurs over and over again many times in a single second. The rapid striking of the clock spring against the contact screw produces the buzzing sound.

You will probably need to adjust the contact point to make your telegraph buzzer buzz properly. Move it up and down slightly until the best results are obtained and then lock it securely in place. The clock spring must be close to the end of the electromagnet but not close enough to touch and stick down. Also be sure to sandpaper or file the contact point and the portion of the clock spring with which it makes contact. All wire connections must be clean and free of insulation.

THE INTERNATIONAL (CONTINENTAL MORSE) CODE

A · —			N — ·
B — · · ·			O — — —
C — · — ·			P · — — ·
D — · ·			Q — — · —
E ·			R · — ·
F · · — ·			S · · ·
G — — ·			T —
H · · · ·			U · · —
I · ·			V · · · —
J · — — —			W · — —
K — · —			X — · · —
L · — · ·			Y — · — —
M — —			Z — — · ·
1 · — — — —			6 — · · · ·
2 · · — — —			7 — — · · ·
3 · · · — —			8 — — — · ·
4 · · · · —			9 — — — — ·
5 · · · · ·			0 — — — — —

PERIOD · · · · · ·   COMMA · — · — · —

Dots and dashes are easy to make with the buzzer. An actual telegraph key makes clicks only, and these are more difficult to interpret. Practice sending the International Code given in the accompanying table. Soon you will be able to send messages to a friend. Do this very slowly at first as it is more difficult to "read" the code than it is to send it.

If you want to telegraph messages to someone in the next room or next door, make another buzzer and another key. Break your circuit open between the buzzer and battery. Extend two wires, one from your buzzer and one from the battery, to the next room. Then connect the second buzzer and key between these two wires. When one key is being used for sending, the other key must be locked down. Both buzzers will buzz. If you add another battery to the circuit, be sure to connect the center terminal of one battery to the edge terminal of the second battery.

25 | Make a Motor

Here are the plans for an easy-to-make electric motor. This simple toy demonstrates the underlying principles to be found in the design of all electric motors.

You should be well pleased to see your motor purr smoothly with only the feeble power input of a small battery. In addition to the battery, you will need a roll of bell wire, two thread spools, a pencil, four large nails at least three and a half inches long, some aluminum foil, and a few odd pieces of lumber.

First find a board about a foot square for the motor base. Sharpen a long pencil at both ends. This will serve as the rotor axle. You will find that the spools will fit snugly onto the pencil.

Saw one spool in half. Tape two of the long nails together, point to head, one on each side of the pencil. Now tape the two spool halves to-

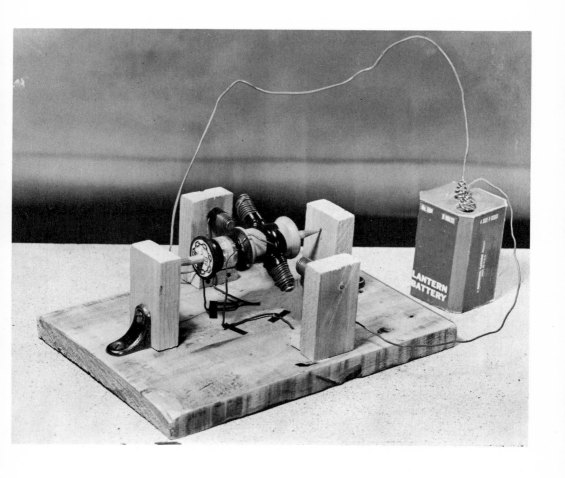

gether, one on each side of the nails. Be sure that the heads of the two nails extend from the spool equally in both directions.

Wrap about forty turns of the bell wire neatly around each end of the pair of nails as shown in the accompanying drawing. The direction the wire is wound is very important. Leave several inches of wire free at each end to fasten to the commutator. The armature of your motor is now complete.

The second spool will carry the commutator and will lie adjacent to the first spool. Prepare two strips of aluminum foil to wrap around the spool. These should be precisely the same length and each should extend nearly halfway around the spool so that there will be gaps of about one eighth of an inch between them. Before taping these foil strips to the spool, remove the insulation from the ends of the armature wires and hook one wire to each of the foil commutator halves. Now tape the foil in place and the commutator as well as the entire rotor assembly is complete.

The sharpened ends of the pencil will serve as bearings for the rotor. Form small indentations in two pieces of wood that will support the rotor at a height that will give clearance for the armature. When these supports are in place, the rotor should turn freely and spin many times around when given a slight push. It is important that the turning rotor be as free from friction as possible.

You are now ready to wind the field coils. Mount the remaining two nails on small vertical boards and wind each nail with forty or more turns of bell wire. The field coils must be wound in the direction shown in the diagram. Leave an ample length of the wire to serve as brushes. Strip the insulation from the ends of these wires. These two bare ends of wire, or brushes, should contact the commutator lightly on diametrically opposite sides. Twist the commutator on the pencil until the brushes touch the spool in the gaps of the commutator when the armature is lined up with the field coils.

The motor is now ready to be hooked to the battery. If you did an extra fine job, your motor will run with the power from several flashlight cells. Perhaps a six-volt lantern battery will be best. You may have to give the rotor a slight push to get it

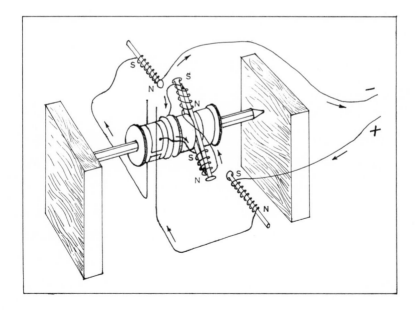

started. Make adjustments in the position of the commutator spool until you find the spot which gives the greatest motor speed.

Now that your toy motor is running smoothly, let's analyze the motor carefully to see how it works. The armature and field coils are electromagnets. Each electromagnet has a north-seeking and a south-seeking end, just as a compass needle has. These ends are called poles. Two south-seeking or two north-seeking poles repel one another. A north-seeking and a south-seeking pole attract one another. The two field magnets are wound so that the ends next to the armature are always magnetized oppositely. The armature is also wound so that its ends are magnetized oppositely. The armature swings around because of the attraction of north-seeking for south-seeking poles.

Just as the armature swings past the field magnets, the commutator connections are switched. This reverses the magnetism in the armature. The armature motion continues now by repulsion. So the motor turns on and on, first by attraction, then repulsion, attraction, repulsion.

The commutator is no more than a simple switch that reverses the magnetism in the armature at the proper moment.

106

You may be able to improve the motor design with better rotor bearings, with more powerful armature and field magnets, or in some other way. Why not try some ideas of your own?

26 How To Stop Flickering Light

Do you think that the light from an ordinary tungsten light bulb is completely steady and shines without a flicker? You're right, it is steady. Is the light from a fluorescent lamp steady in the same way? If you guessed that it is steady, you're wrong. A fluorescent lamp gives off a rapidly flickering light.

A fluorescent lamp turns on and off 120 times a second. The alternating current which comes into our homes is 60 cycles. This means that the current flows in one direction and then in the opposite direction 60 times each second. Since a fluorescent lamp lights up no matter which way the

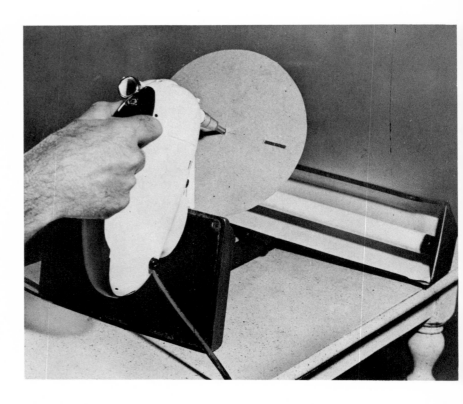

current flows, it comes on 120 times each and every second. Each time the current stops before it turns around and flows in the opposite direction the fluorescent lamp goes off.

Prove this to yourself by constructing a simple stroboscope. You will need an electric mixer and a piece of cardboard. Cut the cardboard into a circular disk six to eight inches in diameter. Near the edge of the disk cut a slot about one eighth inch wide and an inch long that lines up like a spoke in a wheel. Attach the disk to the stem of one beater of the electric mixer.

Now view a fluorescent lamp through the rotating slot in the cardboard disk. Your head should be well back from the disk. A pattern composed of several bright and dark "spokes" will be seen. By careful adjustment of the speed of the motor, the spokelike pattern can be made to stand still. If the motor speed is a little too fast or too slow, the pattern will slowly drift around in one direction or the other.

What happens is this. While the lamp is on during one of its 120 flashes in a second, you see light through the slot in the disk. Then the lamp goes out. When it comes back on 1/120 of a second later, you again see light through the slot, but now the slot has moved an inch or two around from its previous position. This happens over and over again. Each time the lamp is on, the slot is seen, but in a slightly different position each time.

If the lamp is again lit by the time the slot returns to one of its previously illuminated positions, the bright "spoke" seen here, as well as all the others, seem to stand still.

Notice the dark "spokes" in between the bright ones. These mark the positions of the slot during the periods that the lamp is off. The dark spokes will actually appear as a dull orange. This shows that the fluorescent lamp does not extinguish completely in between the brighter flashes of light. A

uniform blur of light would surely be seen if the lamp did not give off a flickering light.

There are a number of different motor speeds which will make the spokes stand still. Fewer spokes will be seen the faster the motor turns. Whenever the pattern is stationary, your strobo-scope has "stopped" the flickering of the lamp so that its rapidly changing light output can be viewed.

Try your stroboscope on an ordinary tungsten filament light bulb. No light and dark spokes ap-pear this time for there is no flickering to stop. The electric current still pulses back and forth 60 times a second, but the bulb does not go out. The expla-nation is this. A tungsten bulb gives off light be-cause the filament glows white hot. The filament simply hasn't enough time to cool and dim its light between surges of electricity.

27 Electricity Drop by Drop

Modern atom-smashing machines produce a stream of tiny bombarding particles of extremely high energy that go crashing and smashing their way through matter in all sorts of interesting ways. These particles are driven at great speed because they are, in effect, subjected to electrical voltages numbering in the billions of volts.

The bombarding particles often start their journey in a Van de Graaff generator that shoves them into the accelerator proper. The crude forerunner of the modern Van de Graaff is the century-old "water dropper" electrostatic generator made by Lord Kelvin.

You can duplicate Kelvin's machine at home with simple equipment that will generate several thousands of harmless volts of electricity with enough oomph to light a small neon lamp—all with a simple drop, drop, drop, of two streams of water.

112

The experiment will require a small neon lamp called an NE-2 lamp. This type of bulb may be obtained at a TV repair shop or supply store, or from a General Electric supplier. Also needed are two plastic tumblers, some aluminum foil, two six-inch lengths of bell wire or its equivalent, and about two feet of rubber or plastic tubing with an inside diameter of one eighth or one tenth of an inch. The tubing can be obtained at a hobby shop or surgical supply store.

Line the inside of the two plastic tumblers with aluminum foil. Do this by first forming the foil over the outside of the tumblers and then fitting it inside. Fold the foil over the lips of the tumblers and trim away the excess. This provides two insulated metal containers into which the water will drop. Alternatively, two metal cans can be used if they are insulated from the table by placing them on paraffin blocks such as those available at groceries for canning purposes.

Roll a double thickness of foil into a hollow cylinder an inch or more in diameter and about an inch long. Fasten the ends together with a paper clip. Completely remove the insulation from a six-inch length of wire and pinch one of the ends over the foil lip of the tumbler and insert the other end under the paper clip on the foil cylinder. Any wire stiff enough to support the weight of the cylinder will do. Make a second foil cylinder and mount it in the same way on the other tumbler.

Bend the wire supporting the cylinders in such a way that each cylinder will be located directly over the other tumbler and about an inch above its lip. The two wires should be kept about an inch apart. Now attach one of the wires from the neon lamp to the center of one of the cylinder-supporting wires. A small air gap should be left between the second lead from the lamp and the other cylinder wire.

Now an elevated reservoir of water is needed. From this reservoir water will be siphoned by the two lengths of hose to drop through the cylinders and into the two tumblers. Drill two holes in a piece of wood to hold the ends of the hose in place about three inches above each cylinder. Two spring-type clothespins can be used to shut off or adjust the flow of water through the hoses. Suck water through each hose, pinch with the clothespin, and place in position. The water dropper is now ready to generate electricity.

The flow of water should be such that the stream from each hose breaks up into droplets inside the

114

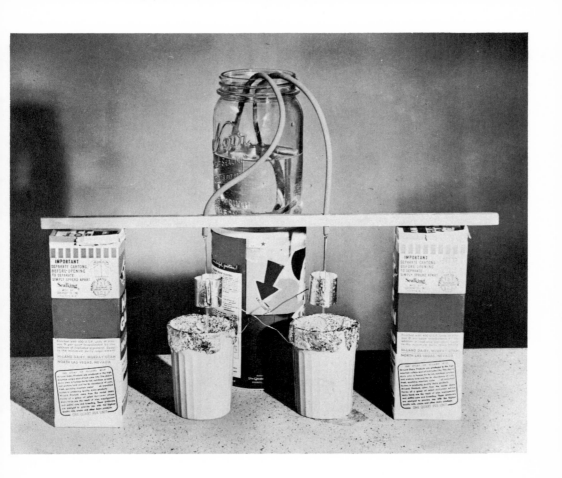

cylinders. This is important. The flow can be controlled if necessary either by pinching each hose slightly or by regulating the height of the water reservoir.

As a starter, the free wire of the neon lamp should be positioned to form a 1/16 to 1/32 inch gap to the second cylinder-supporting wire. When the generator is operating properly, the neon light will flash brightly every second or so depending on

115

the size of the gap between the lamp and the cylinder wire. It may also flash feebly at a very rapid rate. The lamp flashes whenever a spark jumps the gap so that current passes through the lamp. The spark itself can be seen more easily in subdued light.

Let's analyze the operation of the water-dropper electrostatic generator. For the generator to operate, the cylinder over one of the tumblers, together with the tumbler to which it is electrically connected, must be at a slightly different voltage than the other cylinder-tumbler pair. This will always be the case. Ever so slight a voltage difference will start things off.

Suppose that the left-hand cylinder and right-hand tumbler are positively charged. The positively charged left-hand cylinder causes a negative charge to be formed in the stream of water. When the stream breaks into droplets, these negative charges are trapped and collected in the left-hand tumbler. This negative charge is communicated to the right-hand cylinder and helps it to act on the right-hand stream of water in such a way as to positively charge the drops falling into the right-hand tumbler. This action is repeated over and over again as negative charge builds up in the left-

116

hand tumbler and positive charge builds up in the right-hand tumbler.

When the charge has built up sufficiently, the voltage between the two cylinder-supporting wires becomes great enough to produce a spark across the gap at the neon lamp. The spark is a momentary flow of electric charges that also flows through the lamp to make it flash. The larger the gap, the greater will be the voltage buildup before sparking.

28 Rock 'n' Roll Spectrum

A rock 'n' roll record, or any other kind for that matter, can be made to play all the colors of the rainbow.

A phonograph record makes a rather good substitute for a scientific instrument called a diffraction grating. Gratings, like glass prisms, are used to sort the individual colors of any light mixture. The light from many different sources can be analyzed in this way. The rock 'n' roll record cannot only play "Rainbow"; it can play a large variety of other "songs," depending on the light source viewed.

To make your record play without a needle, hold the thin edge very close to one eye. Point the far edge of the record almost directly at the light source to be analyzed. The light must just barely graze the grooves in the record. Now look into the grooves closest to your eye.

An ordinary tungsten light bulb will show a full rainbow of color when viewed in the phonograph-record diffraction grating. You will see not one, but a half dozen or more short sections of rainbow lined up side by side, with the white reflection of the light bulb at the head of the column.

Try 33 1/3, 45, and 78 rpm records. These have different groove spacings and so spread the colors out in varying amounts. Closer groove spacing produces more spread than coarser spacing.

If there are mercury vapor street lights in your vicinity, point the record at one of these. Although this kind of light appears blue-white to the unaided eye it actually is a mixture of bright globs of violet, blue, green, and yellow. These particular colors are characteristic of light from mercury atoms.

Yellow sodium-vapor lights give off almost nothing but yellow. Neon lights and other fluorescent lighting for signs each play their own "theme

song" of color. This identifies the orchestra, or kind of atoms, doing the playing.

A full rainbow of light is given off by hot objects. In addition to tungsten lamps, these include the sun, glowing carbon particles in a flame, and burning embers in the fireplace.

The phonograph record enables us to see all the colors of light individually because of the sorting action of the grooves. Light reflects off each of the ridges. Light that reflects from one ridge must travel a slightly greater or lesser distance to your eye than light that reflects from an adjacent ridge. If light from adjacent ridges is "in step" (this is explained in the experiment "Blow Bubble Colors"), it will show up in your eye. Whether light of a particular color is in step or not depends on the angle at which it bounces off the record grating. Blue is in step with itself for one angle, green for another, and so on.

A real diffraction grating is an extremely powerful instrument. Gratings are used to analyze metals for the amount of impurities they contain, study the behavior of atoms and molecules, observe the nature of the most distant stars and galaxies in the universe, and to do research in innumerable other ways.

29 Nuclear Vapor Trails

One of the most important tools of the nuclear physicist is the cloud chamber. This instrument creates tiny trails of fog which reveal the motion of nuclear particles. These particles may come from powerful accelerating machines, from the natural radioactivity of the earth's crust, or from a distant exploding star.

A diffusion cloud chamber can easily be made at home with the following materials: a wide-mouth glass fruit jar with metal lid, some rubbing alcohol, a small piece of black velveteen, a few cents' worth of dry ice, a small piece of sponge or blotting paper, and a bright light.

The diffusion cloud chamber consists of a closed space which is very cold at the bottom and has a supply of warm liquid alcohol at the top. As the alcohol vaporizes, it drifts slowly downward and a region near the bottom becomes supersaturated with alcohol vapor. The supersaturated vapor is capable of forming threadlike vapor trails when tiny nuclear particles streak by. These trails show up well when illuminated by a bright light.

First, glue a small piece of sponge to the bottom of the fruit jar. Heavy cardboard or blotting paper may be used in place of the sponge. Now line the lid of the jar with a small piece of black velveteen or black carbon paper. This dark background will make the vapor trails show up clearly. Next, cut away an inch-long section from the side of the screw cap. This serves as a window to illuminate the trails which will appear near the black background.

Saturate the sponge with alcohol. Almost any kind of alcohol will do, but you may already have some rubbing alcohol on hand. Invert the jar and set it on a small piece of dry ice. (Look in the yellow pages of your phone book under "Dry Ice" to learn where this material can be obtained. In handling dry ice you must be very careful to hold it in your hand for only a very short time, as it can produce serious burns if it stays in contact with the skin too long.)

After five or ten minutes shine a strong light into the jar through the cut-out section of the

screw top. The beam of light from a home-movie or slide projector is excellent. A flashlight which has a strong beam may also be used. Proper lighting is very important. There must be no glare from the upper parts of the chamber. Seeing conditions will be considerably improved if you block out un-

123

wanted light by covering the front of the jar—
with the exception of the window—with black
paper.

If all goes well, you will plainly see tiny vapor
trails in the bottom quarter inch of the jar. These
last only a moment, then disappear. At times you
will see nothing. At other times you will see several trails at once. Your homemade cloud chamber
has made visible the fleeting paths of nuclear particles from cosmic rays and from the earth's natural radioactivity.

Today bubble chambers are being used exten-
sively to track nuclear particles so that their properties can be studied. A bubble chamber employs
a liquid medium rather than the vapor medium of
a cloud chamber. The trails are made of tiny bubbles instead of liquid droplets. The basic principle
of the two instruments, however, is much the
same.

30 Dominoes and Atomic Fission

Nuclear reactions sometimes multiply by the division of atoms of uranium or plutonium. This is strictly short division, a splitting of heavy atoms into two nearly equal parts.

Multiplication comes in when each splitting atom causes additional atoms to split. If, for example, one splitting uranium atom causes two others to split, these two can cause four more to split, four can cause eight, the eight can cause sixteen, and on and on.

The division of an atom into two roughly equal parts is called atomic fission. This word comes from the field of biology. There it is used to describe the process of cell reproduction which occurs when a parent cell splits, or fissions, to form two other cells. Atomic fission is the process that accounts for the energy of an atomic power plant and the destructive power of an A-bomb.

Get out your set of dominoes. These will help you visualize the fission process. Fission occurs when a minute nuclear particle called a neutron is absorbed into the nucleus of a uranium (or plutonium) atom. The extra neutron is one particle too many in a nucleus already crowded with particles. The nucleus promptly splits, thereby relieving the congestion.

During the split-up, extra neutrons are given off. Each of these neutrons can be absorbed by neighboring uranium atoms to produce other fissions. This kind of self-sustaining process is called a chain reaction.

Dominoes set up on edge in single file can be made to produce a chain reaction. The reaction starts when the first domino is tipped over. Each succeeding domino is knocked over by the one that precedes it. Each tipped-over domino represents a single splitting atom. In this case, only one of the neutrons released with each fission goes on to produce another fission. We say that the multiplication factor of this chain reaction is one. This is the kind of chain reaction that occurs in an atomic power plant. To provide power, many atoms must

be splitting at any given moment, as each splitting atom causes one and only one neighboring uranium atom to undergo fission. In this process fission proceeds at a slow and steady rate.

Set up the dominoes again—this time in a different fashion. Put down one domino and behind it place two others to form a V so that both these will go down when the first domino falls. Set up

the whole set of dominoes in this way, placing two dominoes behind one other.

Now, when the very first domino falls, a chain reaction is produced which builds up at a very rapid rate and the entire array of dominoes falls in a short time. The multiplication factor of this reaction is two. Each of the two neutrons from each fission moves on to produce two more fissions,

these two produce four, the four make eight, the eight cause sixteen, and so on.

A small lump of pure uranium contains trillions and trillions of atoms. When all these are made to split in an extremely small fraction of a second by a chain reaction in which the multiplication factor is two, a tremendous explosion results—the explosion of an atomic bomb.

Scientists must control the division and multiplication habits of uranium or plutonium atoms

very carefully. To make a bomb, the split-ups should multiply very rapidly. For peaceful power production, strict control of the multiplication rate must be maintained to keep the power plant from getting out of hand.

31 Nuclear Drop in a Bottle

Raindrops and nuclear drops try, but they're seldom able to make themselves perfectly round. Raindrops become shaped like teardrops when falling through the air toward the earth. When clinging to your car window or resting on the pavement, they always have a flat side.

Raindrops are never left completely to themselves. They are buffeted about by the various forces of nature, and this always changes their shape from the spheres they would otherwise be.

The nuclei of such heavy atoms as lead, gold, and uranium behave as if they were extremely small liquid drops. Like raindrops, these nuclear drops are also subjected to forces which put them "out of round." Atomic fission, "evaporation" of small particles from the nuclear surface, and collision with high-speed particles—all these distort a nuclear drop from an otherwise perfectly spherical shape.

You can make a large liquid drop that is almost a perfect sphere, for if a liquid drop is isolated from large outside forces, it will assume a spherical form by its own action. Ours will be neither a raindrop nor a nuclear drop, but a beautiful sphere of cooking oil.

Either vegetable oil or olive oil will serve as the drop. Also secure some rubbing alcohol, a medicine dropper, and a small flat-sided bottle.

Fill the bottle about two-thirds full with alcohol. Add enough water to fill about half of the remaining volume of the bottle. Water and alcohol mix to form a liquid which is denser than pure alcohol, but less dense than pure water.

Fill the medicine dropper with cooking oil. Now, with the tip of the dropper under the surface of the water-alcohol mixture, squeeze out some of the oil. The drop of oil will probably float. If this is the case, add more water little by little until the drop neither floats nor sinks, but remains suspended in the center of the water-alcohol mixture.

132

If at first the oil sinks to the bottom, add alcohol until the drop becomes suspended in the middle of the jar. When the drop remains suspended, add more oil until it is the size of a marble.

The cooking-oil drop now is nearly a perfect sphere. It looks like a pale yellow glass marble hanging mysteriously in the middle of the clear liquid.

The drop becomes a sphere because it has been isolated from all outside forces that might distort it. The drop of cooking oil behaves as if it had an elastic film stretched around it. It is this rubbery film which draws the drop into a sphere. A similar stretchy film makes soap bubbles approximately spherical, but these have two elastic films, one on the inside of the bubble surface and one on the outside.

Now that you have a truly round drop, consider it to be the nucleus of a uranium atom. The tiny inner cores of heavy atoms behave in much the same way that liquid drops do. The protons and neutrons of which these nuclei are composed correspond to the molecules of a liquid drop. Molecules can evaporate from a liquid. In like manner, a proton or a neutron can "evaporate" from a heavy nucleus.

134

A liquid drop can vibrate in many different ways. But if the drop vibrates too violently, it may split apart. The best analysis of nuclear fission describes the process in just this way.

Secure some castor oil, which is considerably denser than cooking oil. With the medicine dropper, inject some of this oil into the cooking-oil drop. The two oils will partially mix, but the drop will be seen to sag on its underside due to the denser castor oil. Insert the medicine dropper into the top side of the drop and give the drop a slight wiggle. "Nuclear" fission takes place. The bottom part of the drop splits from the top. Of course, gravity assists here, so the comparison to nuclear fission is not perfect.

Another interesting experiment can be performed with the castor oil. With the large cooking-oil drop suspended in the middle of the bottle, "bombard" it with small castor-oil drops released from the dropper just below the surface of the water-alcohol mixture. The tiny drops of castor oil represent particles from an accelerator such as a cyclotron. Many of the bombarding drops will merely bounce off the sides of the cooking-oil drop, giving it a slight "kick" as they do so. Once in a while, however, a small castor-oil drop will be absorbed by the cooking-oil drop. Both kinds of behavior here are very similar to the action of real nuclei and real bombarding particles.

32 A Hole in the Hand

Would you like to see a hole in your hand the size of a silver dollar? Our eyes often play tricks on us. In scientific observations it is important that we get reliable information from our eyes. This can be done by becoming familiar with some of the idiosyncrasies of vision.

Because we have two eyes we always see double. Each eye transmits a separate image to the brain. If you look at a friend about ten feet away, your eyes focus at that distance. Your brain fuses the two images and your friend is seen as one. Your eyes are not focused on any object closer or farther away and as a result such objects appear double. Fortunately for us, our brains have learned to disregard such double images.

136

A little scientific demonstration will make it appear as if you have a large hole in your hand. All you need is a cardboard tube from a roll of toilet tissue, waxed paper, aluminum foil, or paper towels. Hold the tube in your left hand and look through it with your left eye. Now place your right hand, the palm toward your face, alongside the end of the tube. With both eyes open, you will see a hole in your right hand—a clean, bloodless hole through which you can see objects beyond.

Your brain is unable to concentrate either on the hand or on the hole. The only interpretation it can make is that your hand has a huge hole in it.

33   Seeing Is Disbelieving

The old saying "Seeing is believing" is a lot of nonsense, as the accompanying optical illusions will show. They will demonstrate that our eyes simply cannot be trusted as a measuring device when scientific precision is needed.

In the first figure, there are certainly three offset line segments. Or are there? Sight along the diagonal with your eyes low to the paper.

Do you see six cubes in Fig. 2 or seven? You should be able to see both six and seven, but not at the same time, of course.

138

You may have seen a tile floor that looks something like the third figure. The tiles don't look very straight, but they are.

Fig. 4 shows an equilateral triangle. The sides of the triangle really are straight. Check them with a straight edge if you must be convinced.

The box in Fig. 5 can be made to open up four different ways. Keep looking until you see all four views.

The scissors in Fig. 6 look perfectly normal. Now sight along the length of the lower blade. You've never seen a pair of scissors like this one before.

Fig. 7 shows a different pattern in a tile floor. As drawn, tile "a" is larger than tile "b." If you don't believe it, measure them.

In the last figure, all the vertical lines are straight and parallel.

Try designing some optical illusions of your own. Here's a new twist to try. Can you draw a figure like the one in Fig. 4 except that your triangle will look perfectly straight and normal? Such a triangle, if you can call it that, must have sides that bulge out in the middle. See if you can find other similar illusions, figures that look right only because they are wrong.

34 Beautiful Colors within Your Eyes

Some of the most beautiful colors in the world are to be seen not outside our eyes, but within them. Anyone who has not yet observed the brilliant changing hues of after-images is in for a surprise.

Perform an after-image experiment. You will need no apparatus or instruments other than your own eyes and a bright light. A bare 100-watt light bulb will serve well as a source of white light.

In a darkened room stand so your eyes are about a foot or a foot and a half from the unlighted bulb. Gaze intently at the position of the bulb. Now turn the light on and continue to stare at the bulb for about two seconds without moving your eyes. Turn off the lamp and close your eyes.

You will see a succession of beautifully colored after-images that come and go, changing colors all

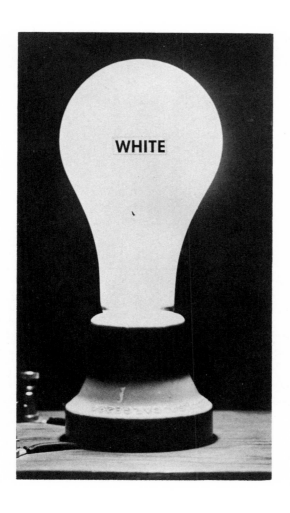

the while. At first you will see a blue reproduction
of the entire bulb with a yellow spot that corresponds to the brightest portion of the bulb. Next,
a bright green patch of light with a red border will
appear. This will change to a red spot with a blue

143

border. Still later a green spot will be seen again, but with a red border surrounded by a second border of blue.

These lovely pulsating colors will continue to come and go for five or ten minutes, or even longer,

depending on the brightness of the original light. Colors that first appear at the edges of an after-image will grow and cover the entire spot of light, the previous color disappearing in the middle. The after-images slowly die away. More blues and pur-

145

ples are seen during these later times. The reds become deeper in hue.

Each person perceives a succession of after-images somewhat different in color and coming at slightly different rates than those perceived by another person. For this reason, it is interesting to perform this experiment with others and compare observations.

The brighter the lamp used, the more intense will be the after-images. A higher wattage bulb or even a movie-projector bulb can be used. If these are used, stand back farther when staring at the lighted bulb.

The setting sun often produces excellent after-images. Exercise extreme caution not to look at it more than a very brief moment. Close your eyes after viewing the sun. You will see after-images of the sun which seem remarkably small. Open your eyes. Again after-images will be seen. If you look in the direction of a bright surface, they will appear dark. These are called negative after-images. Closing your eyes again or viewing a dark surface will reproduce the bright positive after-images.

After-images move with your eye wherever you look. This shows that their cause is to be found within the eye itself. It is generally believed that

146

these images are caused by some sort of interaction on the retina, the screen within the eye on which all things viewed are projected. Fundamental knowledge of the cause of after-images, however, has not as yet been obtained.

35   Find Your Latitude

Lost? You probably don't think so. But do you know the latitude and longitude of your home? Stuck? Then tonight when the stars are out, why not answer half of this question by taking a "shot" of the North Star?

An easy-to-make instrument will determine your latitude by observation of the pole star, Polaris. This instrument can properly be called an astrolabe, the forerunner of today's more elaborate transits and sextants used by surveyors and navigators.

You will need a few odd pieces of lumber, a protractor, a drinking straw, a short length of string, and a metal weight. An inexpensive protractor can be purchased at any store selling school supplies. It will serve to measure the angle from the horizon to the North Star, an angle called the altitude of the star.

First find a small board eight to twelve inches long. Mount it on a base so that it will stand in a vertical position. Also find a second piece of wood about half an inch wide and half an inch thick and cut this to a length slightly longer than the straight portion of the protractor. Nail the center of this second piece to the side and near the top of the vertical board. Don't pound the nail all the way in as the smaller board must pivot freely about the nail. Now mount the protractor on the smaller board, straight section up, and with its 0–180 degree line parallel to the top edge of the board. In order that the center of the protractor arc will be located accurately at the center of the pivot nail, you will have to cut away a small portion of the protractor near the center of its straight edge.

Mount the drinking straw on top of the small pivoting board. This will be a peep sight through which Polaris will be observed. You may prefer to replace the straw with some ingenious sight of your own design. Attach a small weight to a string and

hang it from the pivot nail. This is a plumb bob that will mark the vertical direction on the protractor.

Now find the North Star. This can be done by first finding the Big Dipper. Extend an imaginary

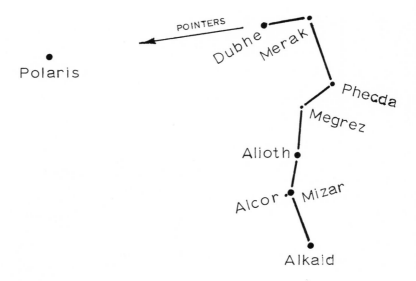

line from the two stars which form the outer edge of the dipper bowl. This line leads almost directly to Polaris.

Sight Polaris through the straw of your astrolabe. This is best done by keeping both eyes open and may take a little practice. As soon as the North Star is centered in the straw, note the reading on the protractor indicated by the position of the string.

The number of degrees from the string to the 90-degree mark is your measured altitude of the North Star. This angle is the same as your latitude. The error in this measurement should be no greater

150

than one degree. For greater accuracy, turn the instrument around and sight through the straw in the opposite direction. Use the average of the two measurements. Now check your latitude measurement with a good map.

Each degree of latitude equals 60 nautical miles, or 69.1 statute (ordinary) miles on the earth's surface. Multiplying your latitude in degrees by 69.1 gives your distance from the equator in statute miles.

A measurement of latitude determines only your distance from the equator—nothing more. All points on an east-west circle around the earth have exactly the same latitude. Such circles are called parallels of latitude. Your latitude is the angle at the center of the earth formed by a line to the equator and a line to your parallel of latitude. To determine your precise location on the earth's surface, you must also find your longitude.

36   Find Your Longitude

Longitude is a measure of one's position to the east or west from an old observatory located at Greenwich, England. It is given in degrees east or west of Greenwich.

To determine your location completely, both the latitude and longitude must be known. The latitude can be found by a shot of the North Star through a homemade astrolabe. This observation locates you somewhere on a line which circles the earth parallel to the equator. Your longitude, on the other hand, places you on a particular north-south line running from pole to pole. Such a line is called a meridian. Your position on the earth's surface is at the crossing point of these two lines.

The first step in finding your longitude is to determine the exact time the sun appears directly in the south. You might think this always occurs at 12 noon. Actually, depending on the time of year

152

and where you live, the sun can be in the south as much as three-quarters of an hour before or after 12 o'clock.

Check your watch to make sure that it shows the correct standard time, not daylight-saving. Now search for a building with straight and flat outside walls lined up directly east-west and north-south. You can check this with a pocket compass. Wait for the sun to move around to a point where its light will just graze along the east or the west wall. On the east, this will occur just a moment before the wall plunges into shadow. At this time on the west wall, the sunlight will just begin to show.

Write down the time this occurs. This is noon according to the sun—but it won't be noon according to your watch for several reasons.

Your watch keeps a kind of sun time, but it runs according to an imaginary sun, not the one you see in the sky. This imaginary sun moves across the sky, day after day, at a uniform speed. This is something the real sun fails to do. Depending on the time of year, the real sun may lag behind the imaginary sun or lead it. In March, the real sun trails the imaginary sun across the sky. We say the sun is slow. It gradually catches up to the imaginary sun, however, and by the end of April the

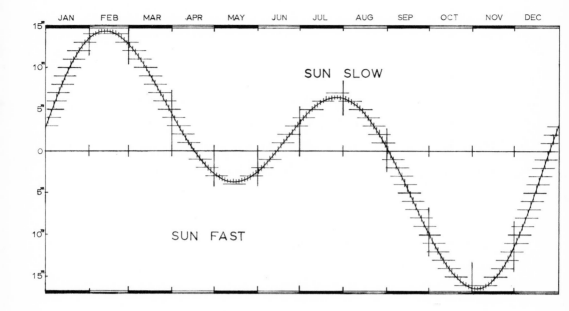

real sun is in the lead. When this occurs, the sun is said to be fast.

The amount by which the real sun is fast or slow compared to the imaginary sun is given in the accompanying chart.

If the sun is slow, subtract the number of minutes it is slow for the day you are doing the experiment from the standard time you observe the sun in the south. This will give the time the imaginary sun was due south of you. When the sun is fast, the amount must be added.

Perhaps you've forgotten the thing we really

154

want from all this is the longitude. There is one more complication. Our clocks and watches keep a kind of time called zone time. Across the United States there are four different zones, each with its own time: Eastern, Central, Mountain, and Pacific. The Eastern zone centers on 75 degrees west longitude, the Central zone on 90 degrees W., the Mountain zone on 105 degrees W., and the Pacific zone on 120 degrees W.

If you live at the center of one of these zones, the imaginary sun will always be directly south at exactly 12 noon. If you live west of the center of a zone, the imaginary sun will appear in the south later than 12. If you live east of the zone center, the imaginary sun will arrive in the south before 12. The time difference between 12 noon on your watch and the time the apparent sun is due south will tell you how far you are to the east or west from the center of your zone.

The imaginary sun moves once around the earth in twenty-four hours' time. Once around is 360 degrees—a full circle. This means that it moves 15 degrees of longitude westward each hour, or a quarter of a degree each minute.

Suppose you found the imaginary sun to be in the south at 12:10. This was determined by cor-

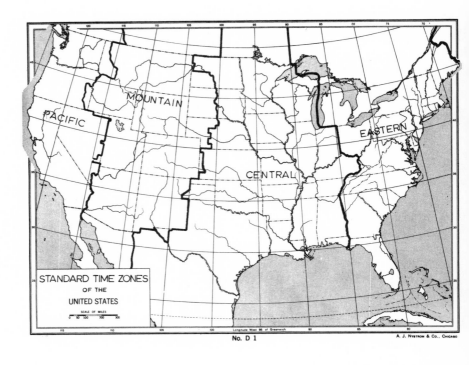

STANDARD TIME ZONES
OF THE
UNITED STATES

SCALE OF MILES
0   50 100   200   300

No. D 1

A. J. NYSTROM & CO., CHICAGO

recting your watch-reading by the amount the sun was fast or slow. You live a quarter of a degree to the west of the center of your time zone for each minute of this figure after 12 o'clock. Your longitude would be 2 1/2 degrees greater than the longitude of your time-zone center. For another example, if the imaginary sun appeared in the south at 11:35, your longitude would be 6 1/4 degrees less than the longitude of the center of your time zone.

Now check your longitude determination with a

156

good map. If you have been careful, you should come within a quarter of a degree of your true longitude. Combine your observed latitude from the previous experiment with your longitude determination to pinpoint your location on the map.

37   Make a Chunk of Blue Sky

Skies are blue, grass is green, and fried potatoes are brown—all this we are likely to take pretty much for granted. But why? Why are skies blue, for instance?

Make a chunk of "blue sky" inside a drinking glass. In so doing you will learn part of the basic behavior of light.

You will need a drinking glass full of water, a little piece of soap—not detergent—a flashlight, a long thin nail, and a small piece of aluminum foil. Dissolve a piece of soap about the size of half a pea in the water. Wait for the solution to become completely clear. This is your blue sky. The next thing you'll need is a sharp beam of light to illuminate it.

Wrap a three- or four-inch strip of aluminum foil around the end of a flashlight. Place the nail directly over the flashlight lens and squeeze the aluminum foil tightly around it. When the nail is withdrawn, you will have a hole which will confine the light to a small, narrow beam.

Now find a completely dark room or closet, the darker the better. You may wish to wait until evening so that a room can be made very dark. Shine the narrow beam from the flashlight horizontally into the soap solution near its upper surface.

Inside the solution the light beam will have a distinctly blue tint. This light is blue for the same reason the sky is blue.

Try shining your flashlight "sunbeams" into a tumbler of plain water. The light beam inside the water will be invisible.

The tiny particles of dissolved soap must be responsible for the bluish beam of light.

You may wish to try other substances in your glass of water. Put several drops of milk into a tumbler of water. An effect similar to that produced by the soap solution is achieved. Now try a pinch of salt or a pinch of sugar. The water re-

mains perfectly clear and will not reveal the presence of the light beam.

Go back to the glass with the soap solution again. The fact that you can see the beam of light inside the liquid means that something there is reflecting light into your eye. This "something" is too small to be seen except by its effect on the light. By moving your head around you are able to see light coming out of the beam in all directions. Scientists call this effect the "scattering" of light.

All well and good, but the blueness of the light is still not explained. The tiny invisible particles of soap inside the solution must somehow treat the blue light differently than all the other rainbow colors which are present in the white beam from the flashlight.

Each of the visible colors of light, violet, blue, green, yellow, orange, and red, differ according to their wave lengths. The wave length of light is a property which corresponds to the crest-to-crest distance between waves of water. The wave lengths of visible light become progressively longer as one proceeds through the spectrum from violet to red. For blue light, for example, this distance is about 16 millionths of an inch. For red light it is about 28 millionths of an inch.

The soap particles dissolved in the water are not much larger than the wave lengths of visible light. The soap particles, however, scatter the shorter wave lengths more efficiently than the longer waves of light. Thus the light which this

160

scattering action sends out of the beam takes on a bluish tinge.

In the sky the process is the same. Tiny air molecules affect the blue light to a greater degree than light of a longer wave length. As a result, more blue light is scattered into our eyes. This scattered light comes to us from all parts of the sky and makes it blue.

38   Measure the Thickness of the Atmosphere

How would you like to measure the thickness of our atmosphere? This sounds as if it might be a difficult undertaking, but in reality it is quite easy.

The instrument that will do the job is called a nigrometer, and you can construct one in just a few minutes.

Satellite measurements tell us our atmosphere extends much farther into space than the several hundred miles previously thought. It has even been suggested that the earth's atmosphere extends so far it envelops the moon, some quarter of a million miles away. Our atmosphere is densest at sea level and, as one moves to higher altitudes, it gradually becomes thinner and thinner.

The first six miles is called the troposphere. The stratosphere extends from this point up to an altitude of about thirty miles. The next twenty-mile layer is called the mesosphere, and beyond this lies the ionosphere, which extends to some 300 miles. The Van Allen radiation belts come next, the outer belt being most intense at an altitude of about 10,000 miles. There is more, but just how much more is not presently known.

The nigrometer will not measure this enormously great extension of our atmosphere. What it will do is this: it will measure the thickness of our atmosphere if all of it were compressed into a uniform layer having the same density throughout as the air at the surface of the earth.

Find a cardboard tube about twenty inches long and an inch or so in diameter. Make lids for both ends of the tube. Make a quarter-inch hole in the center of one of these lids and an eighth-inch hole in the other. Roll black paper around each end of the tube so that it extends several inches beyond the lids.

162

Before proceeding further, let's use the nigrometer in this form to get a clear idea of how it works and what it does. With the smaller hole toward your eye look through the tube at your sunny outdoor surroundings. The two holes restrict your view considerably. Each color in the scene is surrounded by the inky blackness of the inside of the tube and therefore is free from the influence of adjacent colors. Many people notice that colors seem to change when viewed through the nigrometer.

Now aim the tube toward the dark window of a home or building some distance away. As dark a background as possible is desired. You will probably be surprised to notice that a distinct bluish tint is observed through the nigrometer. What you are seeing is light coming into your eye from the direction of the dark window opening. This is sunlight which is scattered in your direction by the air which lies between the dark window opening and your eye. It is a very small section of blue sky.

Move back several hundred yards from the window. The bluish light becomes stronger, for as you move farther from the window the air column becomes longer and scatters more light into the nigrometer.

Now we are ready to measure the thickness of

163

the atmosphere, or more accurately, the thickness of an equivalent uniform layer which would contain the same amount of air as the thousands of miles of ever-thinning atmosphere over our heads.

You will need a small piece of clear glass to mount on the front of the nigrometer. This will reflect light from the blue sky above through the tube. A reflection from the front surface only is desired. This makes it necessary to blacken the back side of the glass. A heavy deposit of soot from the flame of a match will do. The blackening also serves to cut out light coming directly through the glass. A heavily blackened photographic plate would also serve nicely. Cut a slot in the black paper roll at the front of the nigrometer to hold the glass at an angle of about forty-five degrees. The glass should cover just half of the view through the nigrometer.

Point the nigrometer at the dark window opening again. Light scattered from the air between you and the window will be seen in the lower half of your field of view. The reflection of blue sky in the glass will be seen in the upper half. If possible, direct your view so that the sky which is seen in the glass is about sixty degrees from the sun. Move back from the window opening until both halves

of the view are equally bright. You will find that the necessary distance is about 350 to 480 yards.

What you are doing here is comparing the intensity of light scattered by the entire atmosphere to the intensity of light scattered by the column of air between you and the window. The glass, however, reflects only 1/20 of the light from the sky. This means that the sky light is really 20 times brighter than the light reflected from the sky through the nigrometer. Therefore, when the two halves of the nigrometer view appear equally bright, the equivalent thickness of the air above must be 20 times greater than the distance between you and the window.

For example, if you determine that the two halves of your view through the nigrometer are equally bright at a distance of 450 yards from the dark window opening, the equivalent thickness of the air above you would be 20 times 450, or 9000 yards. This is slightly more than 5 miles. If you live a half mile above sea level, this result would be almost exactly right, for the equivalent thickness of air at sea level is very nearly 5 1/2 miles.

Don't expect to come closer than about a mile to the correct result, however, because there are a number of possible sources of error. Dust in the air, for example, can scatter extra light and make the sky appear brighter than it otherwise would.

At any rate, 20 times the distance to the window is the equivalent atmospheric thickness over your head. This distance plus your altitude above sea level should come out to be about 5 1/2 miles, give or take a mile or so.

39   Morning-Glory Gravity

How are a morning-glory hole and a BB like a comet and the sun?

Answer: The motion of a BB around a morning-glory hole is very similar to the motion of a comet around the sun. For that matter, the motion of a planet, a moon, or a satellite can also be duplicated by the tiny BB.

To make a suitable morning-glory hole you will need a large ten-cent balloon, an embroidery hoop, and a nutpick. With a scissors cut the balloon from the neck to the far end. Stretch the rubber tightly across the smaller embroidery hoop and fix in place with the second hoop.

Poke the handle end of the nutpick into the middle of the stretched rubber from the side that is flush with the hoop, tie the rubber to the end of the pick, and pull the nutpick back an inch to an inch and a half below the hoop. Now you have a

167

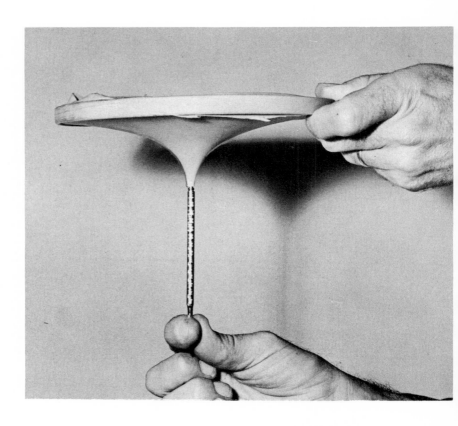

dandy morning-glory hole not unlike that of a real Japanese morning-glory.

Roll the BB comet across the rubber sheet. The morning-glory sun will deflect the comet in a way which depends on the comet's path and speed. If the BB rolls from one edge partly down into the morning-glory hole, turns the corner, and heads back to the edge again, the BB orbit is parabolic and much like that of many comets.

168

Another possibility is for the BB to follow an oval-shaped path around the morning-glory hole. Such a path is similar to the elliptical orbit of planets around the sun, of satellites around the earth, and of certain comets as well.

The dimpled rubber sheet indicates the way the sun's gravity affects the motion of other bodies. The gravitational pull is very strong close to the sun, but becomes weaker and weaker at greater

169

distances. On the model, the slope of the morning-glory hole is very steep near the center, but near the edge it slopes very gently. Of course, it is really the earth's gravity which makes the BB move across the rubber sheet, but the morning-glory shape changes the BB motion so that the tiny ball moves much like a real comet or planet in the solar system.

In the model, the BB moves only on the surface of the morning-glory. In the solar system, objects are not confined to a surface, but may move in any direction which the force of gravity allows. However, with a few limitations, morning-glory "gravity" acts much like real gravity over great distances.

Notice particularly that the BB comet moves much faster as it dips part way down into the morning-glory hole and slows down as it recedes from the hole. Comets speed around the sun this same way, moving with increasing speed as they approach the sun and with ever diminishing speed as they recede. Planets are affected in the same manner, but the speed changes are less dramatic because their orbits are more nearly circular.

Because of the friction between the BB and the rubber, you probably won't be able to duplicate elliptical motion for more than one or two orbits. During one of these times, however, you should be able to clearly see the change in speed along the path.

The earth, for example, moves along its orbit through space faster in the winter when it is nearer the sun than it does in summer when its orbital path carries it several million miles farther away from the sun. Artificial satellites orbiting around the earth change speed in the same way, speeding up as they approach the earth, and slowing down as they recede.

Because of the presence of the sun's huge gravitational "hole," you can see how precarious the earth's orbit really is. If there were as much friction in space as there is on the rubber sheet, the earth would soon dive down into the morning-glory, never to be heard from again.

Rockets designed to travel to a neighboring planet must move at great speed to climb the side of the morning-glory gravity hole surrounding the earth. When it nears its destination, the rocket must descend into the morning-glory hole of that planet. All the while, the rocket must stay clear of the much larger and deeper morning-glory hole of the sun.

171

40   Ballooning Universe

A model of a huge chunk of space is easily made with a ten-cent balloon and a little ink or paint.

The ink or paint is to make spots on the balloon. Each spot will represent a galaxy. A galaxy is a community of stars numbering in the billions and is separated from its neighbors by an average distance of some six billion billion miles.

Before painting on the spots, first partially inflate the balloon. When the spots are dry, inflate the balloon further. Notice what happens to the galaxy spots. The same thing is happening to the billions of galaxies in space. They are getting farther and farther apart. We say that the universe is expanding.

The balloon does not represent the entire universe, but only a small portion of it. The real universe is considered to be everything there is—seen and as yet unseen. It may extend without limit in all directions. Imagine other galaxies than those painted on the balloon, galaxies both inside and outside the balloon. Their behavior is similar to that of the galaxies painted on the balloon's surface.

As you inflate the balloon, notice that each spot, or galaxy, becomes more distant from every other galaxy. Pick a spot. Let this one be our own Milky Way galaxy. All other galaxies seem to be receding from us, moving farther and farther away. Fix your attention on any other galaxy. All the other galaxies seem to be fleeing from this one as well. Each galaxy seems to be at the center of the expansion of the universe, and yet the universe seems to have no center.

Notice also that as the balloon is inflated, two galaxies some distance apart recede from one another at a greater speed than a pair which lie closer together.

These observations agree completely with the observations made on the distant galaxies through our largest telescopes. The galaxies seem to be receding from us, and the greater their distance, the more rapid is their retreat.

On the balloon, the spots will get larger as the balloon expands. In the real universe this does not

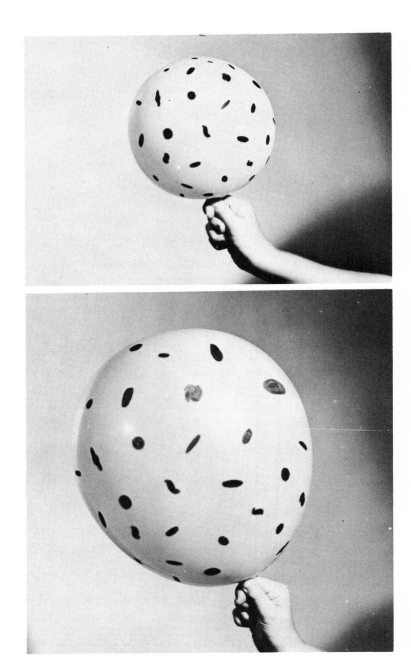

happen. Only the space between galaxies expands.

Astronomers are not yet in agreement as to the meaning of this expansion. It may be that the universe will continue to expand like this forever, each galaxy moving farther and farther away from its neighbors. Then, again, it may be that this expansion will gradually slow down and stop. This would be followed by a contraction of the universe that could lead only to disaster. Still another theory claims that as the universe expands, new galaxies are formed. If true, this process would keep galaxies about the same distance apart for all time.

DR. ROBERT R. KADESCH was born in Cedar Falls, Iowa. He took his B.S. at Iowa State Teachers College, his M.S. in optics at the University of Rochester, and his Ph.D. in physics at the University of Wisconsin. Dr. Kadesch is now an associate professor of physics at the University of Utah and lives in Salt Lake City with his wife and three children.

The experiments in this book originally appeared in the Home Section of the Sunday Salt Lake *Tribune*, for which Dr. Kadesch does two columns weekly. He is the author of a number of technical articles for scientific journals and each year does a series of programs for the University of Utah's educational television station. He also counsels students in their general education program and teaches a workshop in Elementary Science and Science Methods for the Junior and Senior High School for the University of Utah College of Education.

This is Dr. Kadesch's first book.

Set in Linotype Times Roman
Format by Nancy Etheredge
Composition by Brown Brothers
Printing by Murray Printing Co.
Bound by The Haddon Craftsmen, Inc.
Published by Harper & Brothers, New York